THE BOOK OF
TREES

An Introduction to Botany
Through the Study of Trees

Teacher Guide

Sean Brooks

Teacher Note:
Chapters 8 & 9 (Unit V) are considered "Advanced Work," and are optional. Information from these lessons is not included in the Final Exam, but there are optional quizzes and a test for these chapters at the back of this *Teacher Guide*.

MEMORIA PRESS
www.MemoriaPress.com

THE BOOK OF TREES
An Introduction to Botany Through the Study of Trees

TEACHER GUIDE
Sean Brooks

ISBN 978-1-61538-333-7

First Edition © 2013 Memoria Press

Illustrated by Starr Steinbach and Jessica Osborne
Cover illustration by Edward Arthur Walton

Table of Contents

Goals

1. Learn the basic aspects of botany, including plant systems and organs, and their functions.
2. Be able to classify the different types of plants and their external characteristics:

   Two types of plant roots: taproot and fibrous

   Two types of plant stems: herbaceous and woody

   Four types of land plants: trees, shrubs, herbs, and vines

   Leaves: types, textures, shapes, arrangements, venations, margins, simple or compound nature, and buds

   Flower structure and parts: sepal, petal, stamen, and pistil

   Types of fruit: simple, aggregate, and multiple, as well as fleshy vs. dry fruit
3. Be able to identify the internal parts of plant organs, namely the root, stem, and leaf.
4. Learn the basic process of photosynthesis and respiration, as well as the chemical equations associated with each.
5. Learn the processes of pollination, fertilization, and seed dispersal.
6. Be able to classify trees according to their characteristics, and be able to identify them in a guide

Model Lesson Plan

Review

1. Have students name the two plant systems: roots and shoots.

2. Have students list the four major plant organs and their functions.

3. Use a blank diagram of the plant parts learned in last week's lesson and have the students label each part.

4. Quiz (if applicable).

Reading and Questions

1. Read aloud from the assigned text in the lesson.

2. Answer questions as a class or individually. Check the students' answers.

Diagrams and Labeling

1. Diagram internal parts of tree organs.

2. Label different plant types and plant parts.

3. Develop skills for observing and distinguishing plant characteristics.

Activities

1. Take the categories you have learned in the lesson to explore and observe the area around your home or school.

2. Eventually the students will observe trees around the home or school and develop the ability to classify them according to their characteristics. We have included reproducible Trees Observation Worksheets in the Appendix of the workbook. Students should fill one of these out for each tree they observe.*

*The examples given on the answer layer in the Teacher Guide in this section are based on trees found on our school campuses in Louisville, Kentucky. Although these trees may not represent what is present in your area, these will at least provide an example as to how to fill in answers on the observation pages.

It Is Not Growing Like a Tree

Ben Jonson (1573-1637)

It is not growing like a tree
In bulk, doth make Man better be;
Or standing long an oak, three hundred year,
To fall a log at last, dry, bald, and sere:
A lily of a day
Is fairer far in May,
Although it fall and die that night—
It was the plant and flower of Light.
In small proportions we just beauties see;
And in short measures life may perfect be.

UNIT I
The Root & Stem

Lesson 1: Plant Systems & Organs

Reading and Questions

The Book of Trees pp. 5-7

1. What unique ability do plants possess? __Plants have the unique ability to produce their own food__ by harnessing the power of the sun, and they provide oxygen for all living creatures.

2. List some of the uses of trees (both from the text and from your own knowledge and experience). __Trees provide food, shade, give homes to animals, produce oxygen, their wood is used for various__ types of building, baseball bats, tree houses, etc.

3. Why are trees considered a symbol of wisdom and strength? __Trees take a long time to grow__ and mature, and when they do, they produce fruit in season and are able to endure the seasons. Their age and resilience suggest a nature that is prudent and patient.

4. What is an organ? __An organ is a structure of tissue that performs a particular function in an organism.__

5. What is a system? __A system is a group of organs that work together to perform a particular__ function in an organism.

6. List as many of the 11 systems in the human body as you can. __Integumentary (skin, hair, nails),__ nervous, skeletal, endocrine (glands that regulate growth), muscular, cardiovascular, lymphatic (houses white blood cells and removes debris from blood), respiratory, urinary, reproductive, and digestive

7. What are the two systems found in plants? __root system and shoot system__

8. How many organs make up the root system? __1__ What is it? __the root__

9. What are the functions of the root system? __The root system anchors the plant and performs the__ functions of absorbing water and nutrients and storing food.

10. How many organs make up the shoot system? __3__ What are they? __the stem, the leaf, and the flower__

11. What are the functions of the shoot system? __The shoot system holds the plant upright,__ manufactures food, and reproduces the plant by means of seeds.

Diagrams and Labeling

- Label the diagram of plant systems and organs.

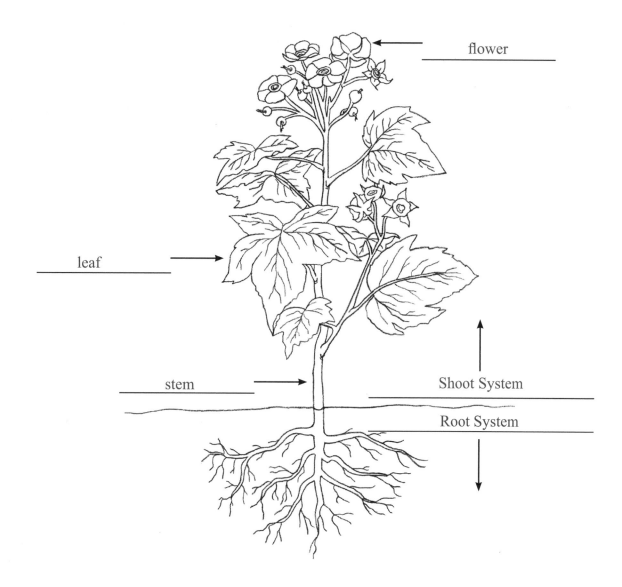

flower

leaf

stem

Shoot System

Root System

Activities

1. Take a walk outside and try to count the different types of plants you encounter just around your home or building.
2. Memorize "It Is Not Growing Like a Tree" from p. 6 of this workbook.

Lesson 2: The Root System

Reading and Questions

The Book of Trees pp. 8-12

1. How do plants attain the water they need to live and grow? __Plants extract water from the__ _ground through their roots._

2. What are the two basic designs for plant roots? _____taproot and fibrous_____

3. What is the difference between these two designs? ____The taproot has one primary root jutting__ _straight into the ground with few roots branching from it. The fibrous root is a wide-spreading mass_ _of roots without a primary root._

4. Trees begin their life with what root design?____taproot_____

5. What are the two types of taproots? _____food-storing and non-storage taproots_____

6. List examples of food-storing taproots (both from the text and from your own knowledge and experience). ____beets, carrots, radishes, turnips, parsnip, rutabaga____

7. What are the benefits of a fibrous root system? __The fibrous root system maintains nutrients by__ _keeping soil from being washed away. It provides a strong and resilient anchoring system for_ _the plant._

8. List the parts of a plant root from outside to inside. __epidermis with root hairs, cortex, and__ _vascular cylinder with xylem and phloem_

9. _____Nutrients_____are minerals and salts that are dissolved in the water the plant absorbs which help the plant grow.

10. The _____vascular cylinder_____ transports water and food in the root. The _____xylem_____ specifically takes the water to the stem, and the __phloem_____ receives the food made in the leaves.

11. What are cells? ___Cells are small units of life that make up larger organisms.___

12. What are the two functions of the cortex? ___The cortex supports the plant root and stores food for__ _later use._

Diagrams and Labeling

- Label the plants according to their root design.

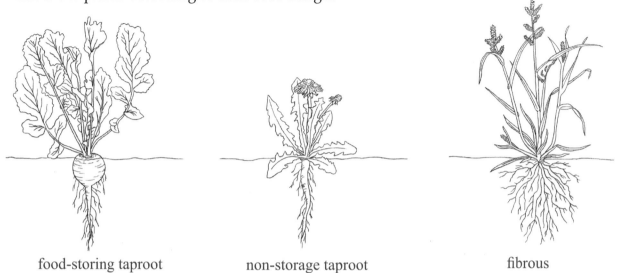

| food-storing taproot | non-storage taproot | fibrous |

- Label the parts of a plant root.

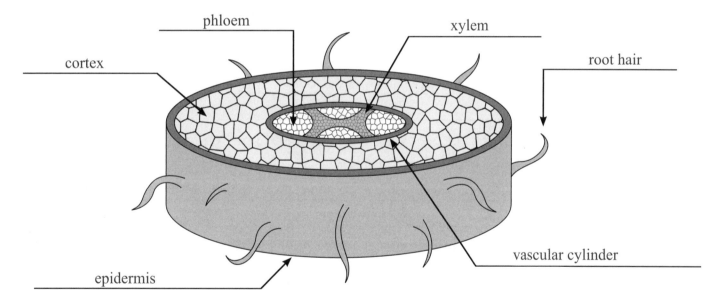

Activities

1. (With permission!) Gently uproot a plant near your house or building and examine its root system. (The larger the roots, the easier the activity.) What type of root system does it have? Can you see the root hairs?

2. Make a cross section (if you are holding the plant vertically, make a cut horizontally) of the root specimen you collected, and using a magnifying glass, see how many parts of the internal structure you can identify.

Lesson 3: External Structure of Stem

Reading and Questions

The Book of Trees pp. 13-18

1. List the functions of a plant stem. The stem supports the leaves and reproductive parts of the plant, transports food and water, acts as a storage facility for food, and sometimes performs the process of making food (rare).

2. A plant whose cells contain _____lignin_____ are classified as a woody plant.

3. What are the two types of plant stems? _____woody or herbaceous_____

4. What are the four types of land plants? _____trees, shrubs, herbs, and vines_____

5. What is an example of an aquatic plant (a plant that lives in water)? _____algae_____

6. Trees and shrubs both have _____woody_____ stems.

7. What is the difference between a tree and a shrub? _____Trees have a single tall stem, whereas shrubs have several low stems branched near the ground.

8. What is the life cycle of a plant? _____A plant life cycle consists of germinating, flowering, producing seeds, and dying.

9. What are the three different life cycles for plants, and how long does each type of life cycle take? _____perennial - lasting more than two years
    annual - completing its life cycle in one year
    biennial - completing its life cycle in two years

10. List some examples of perennial plants. _____trees, shrubs, potato plants, grass, garlic, ginger, mint, etc.

11. List some examples of annual plants. _____corn, wheat, rice, lettuce, peas, watermelon, beans, etc.

12. List some examples of biennial plants. _____onion, parsley, carrots, tomato plants, etc.

13. How can a farmer "trick" a biennial plant into flowering? _____By planting it in the cold, it initiates the second-year phase of growth.

14. Vines can be either_____woody_____ or _____herbaceous_____. Vines that grow on the gound are called _____runners_____, and vines that grow on other plants or objects are called _____climbers_____.

Diagrams and Labeling

- Label these land plants according to their stems.

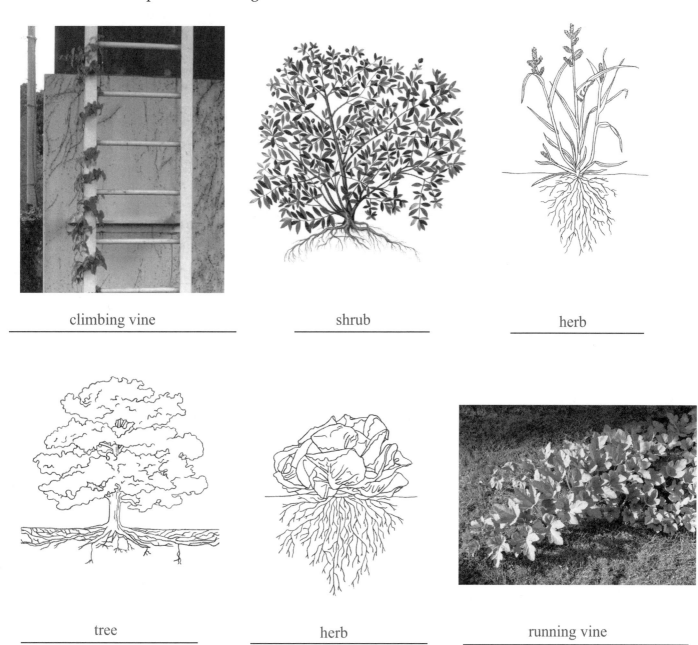

climbing vine

shrub

herb

tree

herb

running vine

Activities

1. Take a walk outside and classify each plant you encounter according to its stem type.

Lesson 4: Internal Structure of the Stem

Reading and Questions

The Book of Trees pp. 18-25

1. The protective outer layer of thickened cells on a herbaceous stem: _____epidermis_____

2. The layer of thinly walled cells that provides structure and stores food: _____cortex_____

3. A thin ring of cells that adds stability and separates the phloem from the xylem: ___cambium_____

4. The spongy inner layer that stores water: _____pith_____

5. What are the three different layers that make up the bark of a woody stem, and what is each layer's function? _____The cork protects the tree from animals and weather._____ The cortex cells store food for the production of more cork. The phloem cells carry food made in the leaves to the growing parts of the stem and roots.

6. What is the sticky substance that flows through the phloem called, and what is it used for? The sticky substance is called sap. Sap is used to make syrup, which is the reason for the existence of pancakes!

7. List some of the different types of bark textures. Some of the textures are smooth, fissured, scaly, and warty.

8. What are the three areas of a woody stem? _____bark, wood, and pith_____

9. Wood is the _____xylem_____ of a woody stem.

10. The difference between the xylem of a herbaceous stem and a woody stem is that in a woody stem, the xylem contains___lignin_____.

11. What is the name of the oldest living tree? _____Methuselah_____ It is _4,800 (4,845)_ years old.

12. What is the function of rays? _Rays give the wood access to the food and nutrients flowing through the phloem.

13. Hard rings of wood that no longer carry water are called_____heartwood_____, while rings that still carry water are called_____sapwood_____.

14. What is the difference between pith in a herbaceous stem and a woody stem? The pith in both herbaceous and woody stems store water. However, in a woody stem the pith is only present in a young stem and eventually disappears.

Diagrams and Labeling

- Label the parts of a herbaceous stem.

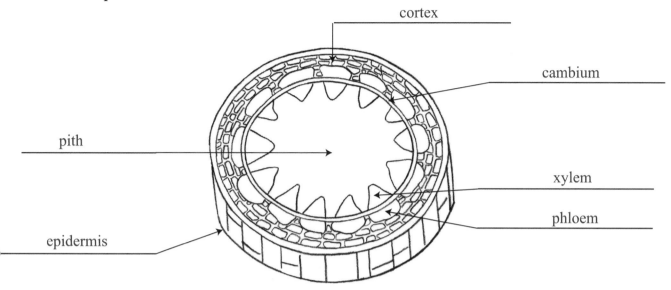

- Label the parts of a woody stem.

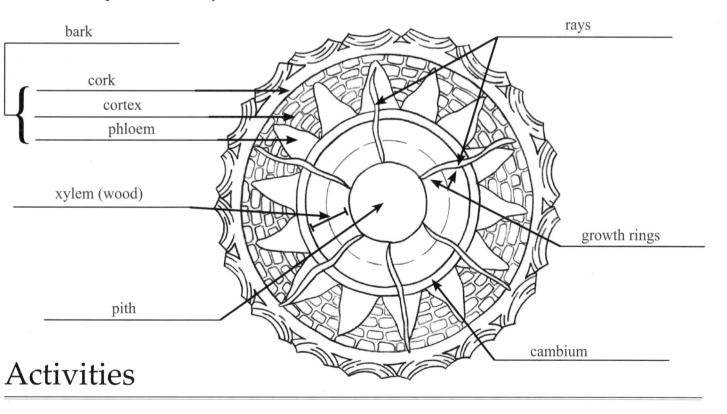

Activities

1. Make a cross section of both a herbaceous and woody stem (the woody stem will require a saw, so make sure you have an adult with you). Examine both and see how many parts you can identify.
2. Take a walk outside and identify different colors and textures of bark on any trees you encounter.

Lesson 5: Unit I Review

Questions

1. What is an organ? __A structure of tissue that performs a particular function in an organism__

2. What is a system? __A group of organs that work together to perform a particular function__

3. What are the two systems found in plants? __root and shoot__

4. What system anchors the plant to the ground and absorbs water and nutrients? __root system__

5. What system holds the plant upright, manufactures food, and reproduces the plant by means of seeds? __shoot system__

6. What are the three organs that make up the shoot system? __stem, leaf, and flower__

7. What are the two basic designs for plant roots? __taproot and fibrous__

8. What are the two types of taproots? __food-storing and non-storage taproots__

9. __xylem__ carry water absorbed in the roots to the rest of the plant.

10. __phloem__ carry food made in the leaves to the stem and the roots.

11. What are cells? __Cells are small units of life that make up larger organisms.__

12. What organ supports the leaves and reproductive parts of the plant, transports food and water, and acts as a storage facility for food? __stem__

13. What are the two types of plant stems? __herbaceous and woody__

14. What are the four types of land plants? __trees, shrubs, herbs, and vines__

15. What is the life cycle of a plant? __germinating, flowering, producing seeds, and dying__

16. A plant life cycle that takes one year to complete: __annual__

17. A plant life cycle that takes two years to complete: __biennial__

18. A plant life cycle that takes more than two years to complete: __perennial__

19. The protective outer layer of thickened cells on a herbaceous stem: __epidermis__

20. The layer of thinly walled cells that provides structure and stores food: __cortex__

21. A thin ring of cells that separates the phloem from the xylem and makes new xylem in woody plants: __cambium__

22. The spongy inner layer that stores water and eventually disappears in woody plants: __pith__

23. What are the three different layers that make up the bark of a woody stem? __cork, cortex, and phloem__

24. What is the sticky substance that flows through the phloem? __sap__

25. The substance found in the xylem of woody stems: __lignin__

Diagrams and Labeling

- Label the parts of a root.

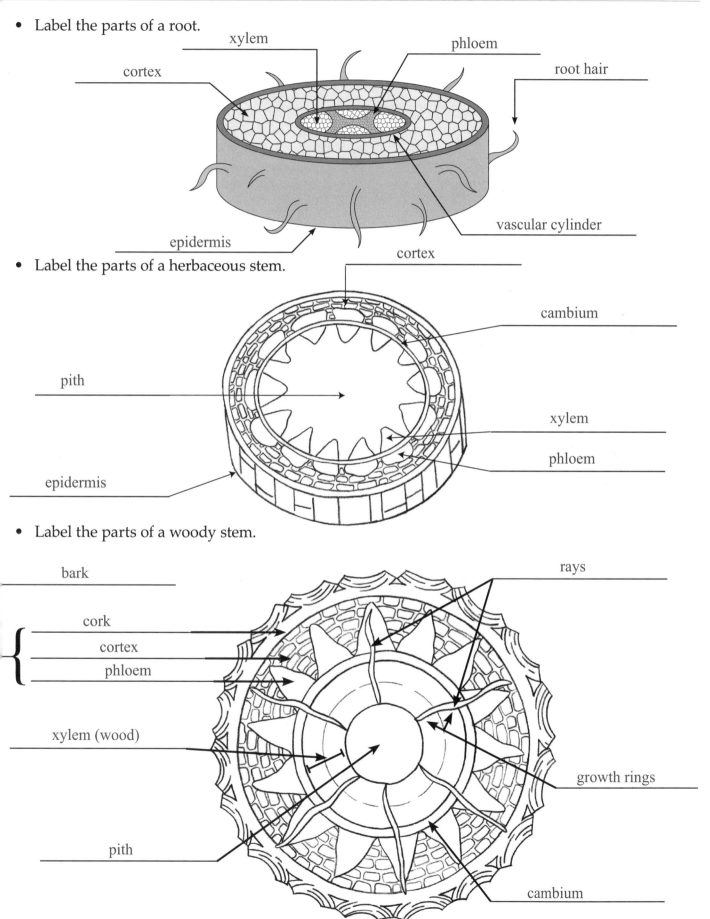

cortex

xylem

phloem

root hair

epidermis

vascular cylinder

- Label the parts of a herbaceous stem.

cortex

cambium

pith

xylem

phloem

epidermis

- Label the parts of a woody stem.

bark

rays

cork

cortex

phloem

xylem (wood)

growth rings

pith

cambium

UNIT II
Leaves

Lesson 6: External Structure of Leaves I

Reading and Questions

The Book of Trees pp. 27-31

1. What are the two major categories of leaves? <u>broadleaf and needle-leaf</u>

2. Why do some trees shed their leaves? <u>Most leaves are too delicate to survive the winter and</u> <u>continue to produce food. In preparation for the winter, the tree sheds its leaves and stores food. Like</u> <u>some animals, the tree slows its internal processes and goes into a state of hybernation for the winter.</u>

3. Trees that lose their leaves in the winter are called <u>deciduous</u>, and trees that keep their leaves in the winter are called <u>evergreen</u>.

4. A tree with needle-leaves is called a <u>conifer</u>.

5. True (False)   All evergreens are conifers.

6. What is the difference between hardwood and softwood? <u>Hardwood comes from trees with</u> <u>broadleaves, and softwood comes from trees with needle-leaves.</u>

7. Why is this distinction a misnomer? <u>Some conifers have wood that is actually harder than some</u> <u>broadleaf trees. Thus, the terms "hardwood" and "softwood" are confusing or poorly given names.</u>

8. What is the primary function of the leaf? <u>The primary function of the leaf is to produce food for</u> <u>the rest of the plant by means of photosynthesis.</u>

9. Most land plants have what type of leaf? <u>broadleaf</u>

10. What are the two parts of a broadleaf? <u>petiole and blade</u>

11. A leaf that has no petiole is called <u>sessile</u>.

12. The process of making food in the leaf is called <u>photosynthesis</u>, and requires <u>sunlight</u> and <u>water</u>.

13. List the different leaf textures. <u>smooth, rough, fuzzy, hairy, or waxy</u>

14. List the various aspects used by scientists to categorize the different types of leaves. <u>type, texture, shape, arrangement, venation, margins, and whether it is simple or complex</u>

15. List the nine different leaf shapes. <u>linear, oval, oblong, ovate, lanceolate, elliptical, cordate,</u> <u>deltoid, and spatulate</u>

Diagrams and Labeling

- Label the leaf type.

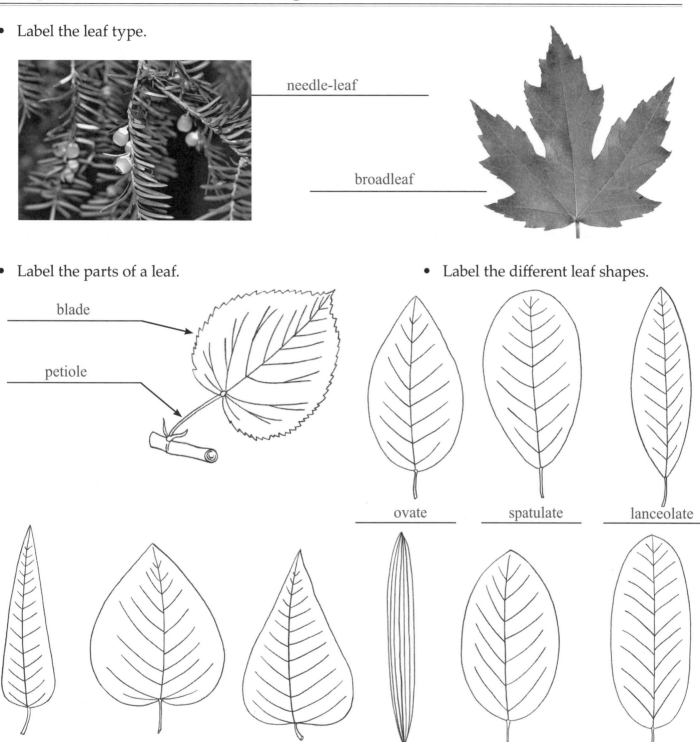

needle-leaf

broadleaf

- Label the parts of a leaf.

blade

petiole

- Label the different leaf shapes.

ovate

spatulate

lanceolate

elliptical

cordate

deltoid

linear

oval

oblong

Activities

1. See who can find the most of the nine leaf shapes around your school or home, or see how many different leaf shapes you can find in 10 minutes.

2. (Besides grass) See if you can hunt down a plant that has sessile leaves.

Lesson 7: External Structure of Leaves II

Reading and Questions

The Book of Trees pp. 32-37

1. Leaf arrangement is determined by the number of _____leaves_____ at each _____node_____.

2. List the three types of leaf arrangement and note how many leaves each has per node. _____
   _____alternate: one leaf per node_____opposite: two leaves per node_____
   _____whorled: three or more leaves per node_____

3. Venation refers to the arrangement of _____veins_____ in the leaf blade, and these vascular structures contain the _____xylem_____ and _____phloem_____.

4. The main vein in a pinnate leaf is called the _____midrib_____.

5. Pinnate means: _____"like a feather"_____

6. Palmate means: _____"like a palm"_____

7. The outer edge of a leaf blade is called the _____margin_____.

8. What is the difference between a simple and a compound leaf? __A simple leaf has one blade for
   every petiole. A compound leaf has multiple blades for every petiole._____
   _____
   _____

9. The main vein in a compound leaf is called the _____rachis_____, and the multiple blades are called _____leaflets_____.

10. The angle at which the leaf grows from the branch is called the _____axil_____.

11. Into what can a leaf bud grow? ____a new leaf, a new branch, or a flower_____
    _____

Diagrams and Labeling

- Label the different types of leaf arrangement.

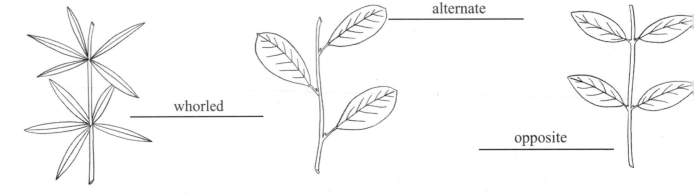

alternate

whorled

opposite

- Label the different types of leaf venation and the midrib.

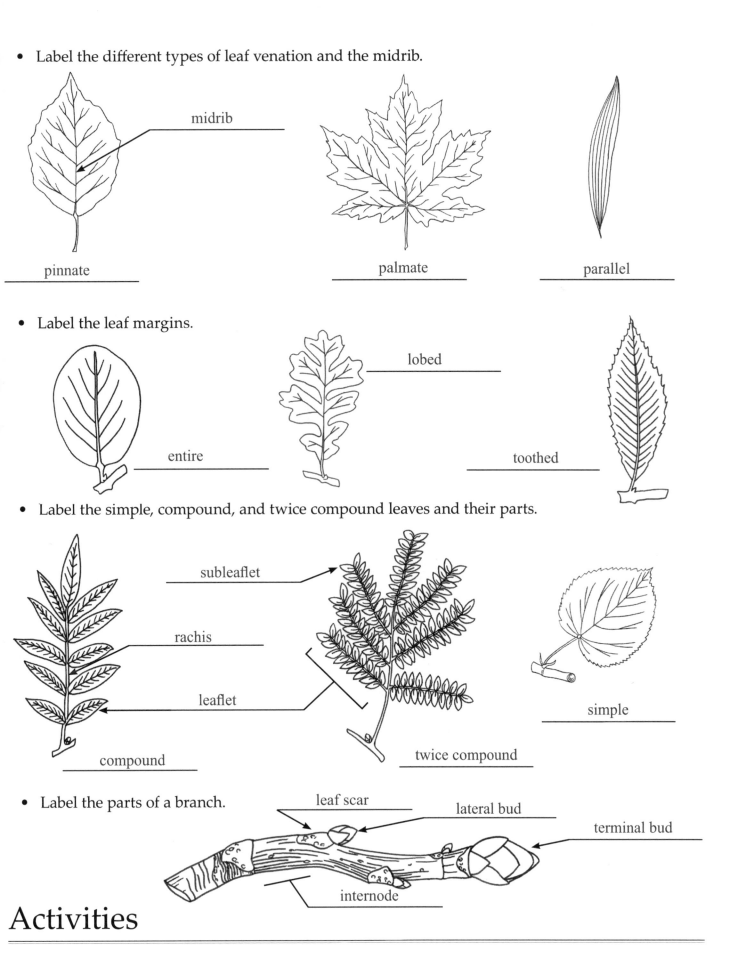

midrib

pinnate

palmate

parallel

- Label the leaf margins.

lobed

entire

toothed

- Label the simple, compound, and twice compound leaves and their parts.

subleaflet

rachis

leaflet

compound

twice compound

simple

- Label the parts of a branch.

leaf scar

lateral bud

terminal bud

internode

Activities

1. Find 5-6 examples of leaves and categorize them according to their arrangement, margin, and whether they are simple, compound, or twice compound (bi-pinnate).

Lesson 8: Internal Structure of Leaves

Reading and Questions

The Book of Trees pp. 37-41

1. What is the primary function of leaves? _____ to produce food for the plant

2. The outermost layers of the leaf are called the _____ upper epidermis _____ and the _____ lower epidermis _____, and both are covered with a waxy layer called the _____ cuticle _____.

3. What are stomata? _____ Stomata are thousands of small openings in the lower epidermis of a leaf that _____ allow air to enter the leaf. _____

4. What three elements are required for photosynthesis? _____ sunlight, water, and CO_2 _____

5. _____ Guard cells _____ open and close the stomata so that the leaf doesn't dry out.

6. The cells that give color to the leaf are called _____ mesophyll _____.

7. The upper layer of mesophyll is called the _____ palisade _____ layer, and the lower layer of mesophyll is called the _____ spongy _____ layer.

8. What makes leaves green? _____ The mesophyll has food-making factories called chloroplasts that have _____ the green enzyme called chlorophyll. The chlorophyll is where photosynthesis takes place and is _____ what gives the leaf its green color. _____

9. When do other pigments in the leaf become visable? _____ When the chloroplasts stop performing _____ the process of photosynthesis, the chlorophyll disperses and other pigments in the leaf are seen. _____

10. Why are evergreens "evergreen"? _____ Evergreen trees continue to perform the process of _____ photosynthesis even in winter, and thus always remain green. _____

11. In plants other than trees, what do brown, withered leaves mean? _____ It means that the plant _____ isn't getting sufficient water, sunlight, minerals, or CO_2, and is dying. _____

Diagrams and Labeling

- Label the internal parts of a leaf.

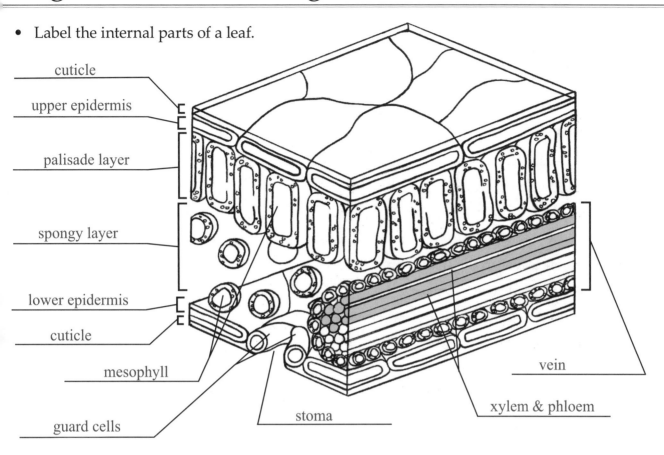

cuticle

upper epidermis

palisade layer

spongy layer

lower epidermis

cuticle

mesophyll

guard cells

stoma

vein

xylem & phloem

Activities

1. **Leaf Pigment Experiment** (takes 1 1/2 - 3 hours to complete)
   Materials you will need: drinking glasses, rubbing alcohol, a large dish, tape, coffee filters (or filter paper), and popsicle sticks (or pencils)

   Step 1: Collect deciduous leaves (that are still green) from 4-5 trees (a few from each tree).

   Step 2: Tear the leaves up and place them in the glasses (labeling each one with the tree from which the leaf came).

   Step 3: Pour the rubbing alcohol into the glasses until it just covers the leaves.

   Step 4: Fill the large dish with warm water and place the glasses in the warm water for 30 minutes (until the alcohol absorbs all the green in the leaves).

   Step 5: Take the coffee filters and cut them into about 1"-wide strips. Tape these strips to the popsicle sticks and rest them on the glasses so that one end of the filter strip hangs in the alcohol solution.

   Step 6: As the alcohol solution slowly absorbs up the filter, the green will start to break up, and after 30-90 minutes, you should be able to see the pigments that were hidden by the chlorophyll. Compare the different pigments found in your specimens.

Lesson 9: Unit II Review

Questions

1. What are the two major categories of leaves? _____ broadleaf and needle-leaf _____

2. Why do some trees shed their leaves? _____ Most leaves are too delicate to survive the winter and continue to produce food. In preparation for the winter, the tree sheds its leaves and stores food. Like some animals, the tree slows its internal processes and goes into a state of hybernation for the winter.

3. Trees that lose their leaves in the winter are called _____ deciduous _____, and trees that keep their leaves in the winter are called _____ evergreen _____.

4. A tree with needle-leaves is called a _____ conifer _____.

5. True / (False)   All evergreens are conifers.

6. A leaf that has no petiole is called _____ sessile _____.

7. The primary function of a leaf is to produce _____ food _____ through the process called _____ photosynthesis _____.

8. This process requires _____ sunlight _____, _____ water _____, and _____ CO_2 _____.

9. Venation refers to the arrangement of _____ veins _____ in the leaf blade, and these vascular structures contain the _____ xylem _____ and _____ phloem _____.

10. Pinnate means: _____ "like a feather" _____

11. Palmate means: _____ "like a palm" _____

12. A simple leaf has one _____ blade _____ for every _____ petiole _____, whereas a compound leaf has multiple _____ blades _____ for every _____ petiole _____.

13. The angle at which the leaf grows from the branch is called the _____ axil _____.

14. Into what can a leaf bud grow? _____ a new leaf, branch, or flower _____

15. What is the function of the stomata? _____ The stomata open and close in order to take in the CO_2 and release oxygen. _____

16. Mesophyll cells have little food-making factories called _____ chloroplasts _____ that contain the enzyme _____ chlorophyll _____, which performs the process of photosynthesis and gives leaves their green color.

Diagrams and Labeling

- Label the different leaf shapes.

A 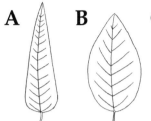 B 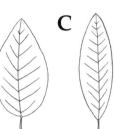 C  D 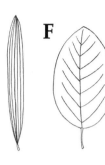 E  F 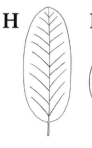 G H  I

A. _____elliptical_____ D. _____deltoid_____ G. _____spatulate_____

B. _____ovate_____ E. _____linear_____ H. _____oblong_____

C. _____lanceolate_____ F. _____oval_____ I. _____cordate_____

- Label the parts of a broadleaf.

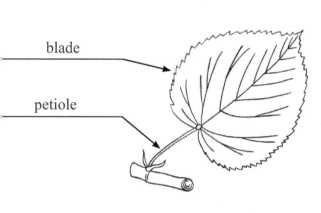

blade

petiole

- Label the parts of a branch.

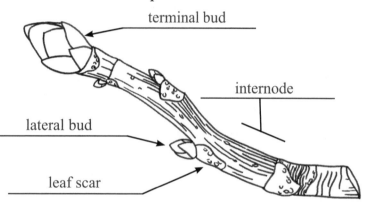

terminal bud

internode

lateral bud

leaf scar

- Label the different types of leaf venation and the midrib.

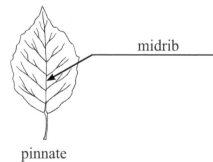

midrib

_____pinnate_____ _____palmate_____ _____parallel_____

- Label the leaf margins.

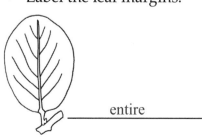

lobed

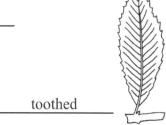

_____entire_____ _____toothed_____

27

- Label the different types of leaf arrangement.

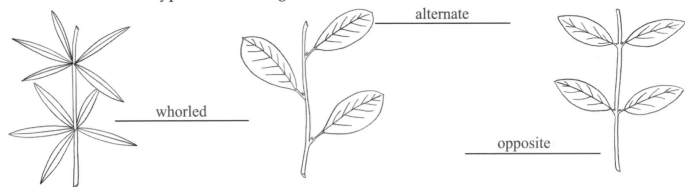

alternate

whorled

opposite

- Label the simple, compound, and twice compound leaves and their parts.

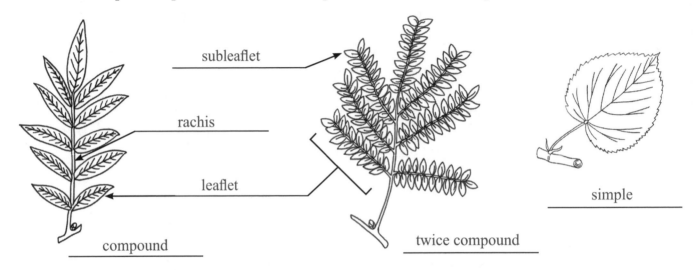

subleaflet

rachis

leaflet

compound

twice compound

simple

- Label the internal parts of a leaf.

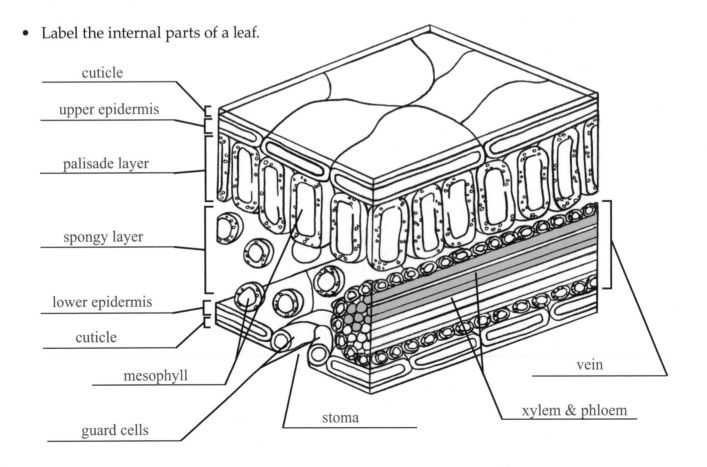

cuticle

upper epidermis

palisade layer

spongy layer

lower epidermis

cuticle

mesophyll

guard cells

stoma

vein

xylem & phloem

UNIT III
Flowers & Fruits

Lesson 10: Structure of Flowers & Perfect Flowers

Reading and Questions

The Book of Trees pp. 43-47

1. What is the function of flowers? Flowers produce seeds in order for the plant to reproduce.

2. The process of producing organisms according to its kind: reproduction

3. What are the four parts of a flower? the sepal, petals, stamen, and pistil

4. A flower grows out of a bud.

5. Protective leaf-like appendages: sepals

6. Why are flowers' petals so colorful? The different-colored flower petals attract different insects and animals to the flower's pollen.

7. A flower's collection of petals is called its corolla.

8. The male part of the flower is called the stamen, and is responsible for producing pollen.

9. What are the two parts of the male part of the flower? filament and anther

10. The female part of the flower is called the pistil, and contains the ovary, which produces the egg cells necessary for the production of seeds.

11. What are the three parts of the female part of the flower? the ovary, stigma, and style

12. Flowers are attached to the stem by the peduncle.

13. The receptacle protects the ovary until it develops into a fruit.

14. What is a botanist? a scientist that studies plants

15. What is a perfect flower? It is a flower with both male and female parts.

16. A flower that only has the male part is called staminate.

17. A flower that only has the female part is called pistillate.

18. Both of these kinds of flowers are considered incomplete.

19. Instead of flowers, conifers produce seeds by means of cones.

20. All conifers have both male and female cones.

Diagrams and Labeling

- Label the parts of a flower.

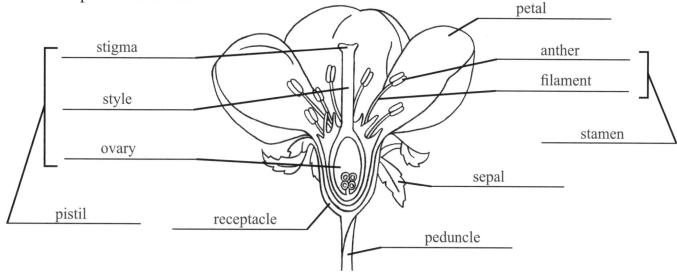

stigma

style

ovary

pistil

petal

anther

filament

stamen

receptacle

sepal

peduncle

- Label the types of flowers.

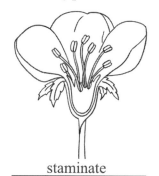  

staminate

perfect

pistillate

- Label the male and female cones.

male

female

Activities

1. If there are any flowers in bloom in your area, take a walk outside and see if you can find a perfect flower, a staminate flower, and a pistillate flower. Identify all the parts of each flower you find.

2. If there is a conifer in your area, see if you can identify the male and female cones.

3. If there are no flowers in bloom in your area, go to a flower shop and identify flower parts and different types of flowers.

Lesson 11: Pollination & Fertilization

Reading and Questions

The Book of Trees pp. 47-49

1. Male reproductive cells are called _____sperm cells_____.

2. What is pollination? _It is the process in which pollen is transferred from the anther to the stigma._

3. Pollination primarily occurs with the help of ___insects___ and ___animals___

4. The sweet-tasting watery liquid produced by some flowers: ___nectar___

5. Bees use the nectar to make _____honey_____.

6. Why is the nectar located at the bottom of the flower? _In order for an insect or animal to get to_ the nectar, it must rub up against the anther, getting pollen on its body. When the insect or animal goes to feed at another flower, the pollen on its body will rub off on the stigma of the other flower, thus pollinating it.

7. Pollination that occurs by the help of a living thing: ___biotic___

8. Pollination that occurs without the help of a living thing is called ___abiotic___ and includes ___wind___ and ___water___.

9. ___Biotic___ pollination is more common than ___abiotic___ pollination.

10. The uniting of the sperm cells with the egg cells is called ___fertilization___.

11. Fertilized egg cells will develop into ___seeds___.

Diagrams and Labeling

- Label the parts of a flower during fertilization.

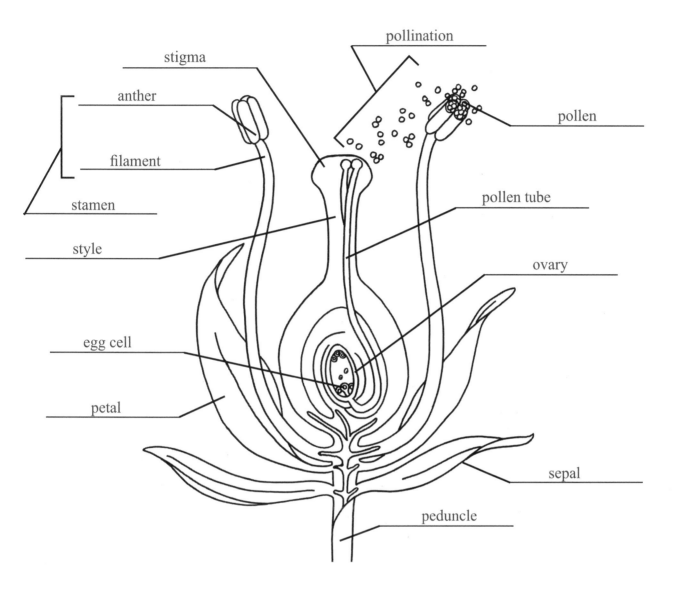

Activities

1. Find a perfect flower (or a staminate flower and a pistillate flower) and (with help!) dissect the flower by removing the petals and cutting through the middle of the receptacle to expose the ovary. Try to locate plant eggs, or perhaps already growing seeds. Also rub the anther between your fingers and examine the pollen.

2. Spend some time outside in an area with multiple blooming plants (or go to a nearby zoo or butterfly house) and observe insect pollination. Note the different pollinators (bees, butterflies, birds, etc.) and pay attention to which plant each prefers. What can you induce about the color or shape preferences of certain pollinators?

Lesson 12: Simple Fleshy Fruits

Reading and Questions

The Book of Trees pp. 51-54

1. Fruit develops from the _____ovary_____ of the flower.

2. What is the function of a fruit? _____The fruit provides protection for the seeds as they grow and_____ then helps distribute the seeds once they are mature.

3. What is the botanical definition of a fruit? _____A fruit is a seed-bearing structure that results from the_____ fully developed ovary of the flower of a plant.

4. What does "culinary" mean? _____"having to do with the kitchen"_____

5. What is the culinary definition of a fruit? _____A "kitchen fruit" is a seed-bearing structure that_____ is sweet in taste and fleshy in composition.

6. What are the three categories of fruit? _____simple fruits, aggregate fruits, and multiple fruits_____

7. Botanists organize fruits into these categories based on how they _____develop_____ and the number of _____ovaries (or pistil)_____ the flower has.

8. A fruit that grows from a single flower with a single pistil is called a _____simple fruit_____.

9. What are the two types of simple fruit? _____fleshy and dry_____

10. A simple fruit that is fleshy and juicy throughout: _____berry_____

11. A simple fruit that is fleshy with a woody pit in the center: _____drupe_____

12. The pit is called a _____stone_____, and this fruit is sometimes called _____stone fruit_____.

13. A simple fruit that is fleshy with a papery inside layer: _____pome_____

14. An apple is formed from the entire _____receptacle_____ of the flower.

Diagrams and Labeling

- Label the following fruits according to whether they are berries, drupes, or pomes, and whether they are considered culinary fruits, culinary vegetables, or culinary nuts.

1. almond ___drupe; nut___

2. watermelon ___berry; fruit___

3. apple ___pome; fruit___

4. peach ___drupe; fruit___

5. pumpkin ___berry; vegetable___

6. walnut ___drupe; nut___

7. cherry ___drupe; fruit___

8. olive ___drupe; vegetable___

9. grape ___berry; fruit___

10. kiwi ___berry; fruit___

11. pear ___pome; fruit___

12. cucumber ___berry; vegetable___

13. avocado ___berry; vegetable___

14. coffee ___drupe; nut or bean___

15. bell pepper ___berry; vegetable___

16. tomato ___berry; vegetable___

Activities

1. Go to the grocery store and procure 1-2 examples of a berry, a drupe, and a pome. (With help!) Cut these fruits in half and examine their differences. Taste each fruit and evaluate them according to how sweet they are.
2. Survey 5-10 people you know (kids in your class don't count) and ask them whether a tomato is a vegetable or a fruit. Keep a tally and then compare to others in your class.
3. Procure a tomato and two other berries, one sweet (grape, orange, watermelon, etc.) and one more savory (cucumber, bell pepper, avocado, etc.). Sample all three fruits and decide for yourself whether the tomato fits better with the culinary fruits or the culinary vegetables. If in a class setting, put it to a vote.

Lesson 13: Simple Dry Fruits; Aggregate & Multiple Fruits; Seed Dispersal

Reading and Questions

The Book of Trees
pp. 54-58

1. What are the five varieties of dry fruits? _____ legumes, samaras, nuts, achenes, and grains _____

2. A simple dry fruit that consists of a pod enclosing several seeds: _____ legume _____

3. These pods can be _____ woody _____ or _____ herbaceous _____.

4. A seed with a papery wing that causes it to spin away from the tree: _____ samara _____

5. A simple dry fruit in which the seed is enclosed by a thick shell: _____ nut _____

6. A simple dry fruit with a thin shell that is mistaken for the nut: _____ achene _____

7. A simple dry fruit that comes from grass and has a thin shell that is attached to the seed: _____ grain _____

8. Why is breakfast cereal called cereal? _____ Breakfast cereal is made from barley, rye, corn, and _____ wheat, which are called cereal grains. _____

9. The process of separating grain seeds from their shells is called _____ milling _____.

10. A cluster of individual fruit structures grown from the same flower: _____ aggregate fruit _____

11. The structure on the outside of a strawberry is an _____ achene _____.

12. A compound fruit that develops from a cluster of individual flowers: _____ multiple fruit

Diagrams and Labeling

- Label the following fruits according to whether they are legumes, samaras, nuts, achenes, grains, aggregate fruits, or multiple fruits.

1. sunflower seed achene

2. peanut legume (woody)

3. raspberry aggregate fruit

4. fig multiple fruit

5. maple tree seed samara

6. hazelnut nut

7. green beans legume

8. barley grain

9. pineapple multiple fruit

10. acorn nut

11. wheat grain

12. stawberry aggregate fruit

13. dandelion seed achene

14. rice grain

15. ash tree seed samara

16. blackberry aggregate fruit

Activities

1. By now you should be able to classify almost everything in the produce aisle at the grocery store. Take a trip to the store and test what you have learned by classifying all the different fruits and vegetables according to their botanical categories.

2. In a classroom setting, the teacher can bring in multiple specimens of each dry fruit category and have the students sort them out into their respective categories.

3. Take a handful of assorted nuts and separate the seeds or stones of fleshy fruits from the true nuts (you may need to research which nuts are which). Once you have separated them, crack them and pay attention to the differences between a nut shell and a stone. Once you are done observing them, enjoy eating the *fruit* of your labor.

Lesson 14: Unit III Review

Questions

1. What is the function of flowers? ___Flowers produce seeds in order for the plant to reproduce.___
   _____

2. The process of producing organisms according to its kind: ___reproduction___

3. What are the four parts of a flower? ___the sepal, petals, stamen, and pistil___

4. Protective leaf-like appendages:___sepals___

5. A flower's collection of petals is called its ___corolla___.

6. The male part of the flower is called the ___stamen___, and is responsible for producing ___pollen___.

7. The female part of the flower is called the ___pistil___, and contains the ___ovary___, which produces the ___egg cells___ necessary for the production of seeds.

8. Flowers are attached to the stem by the ___peduncle___.

9. The ___receptacle___ protects the ovary until it develops into a fruit.

10. A flower that has both male and female parts is called ___perfect___.

11. A flower that only has the male part is called ___staminate___.

12. A flower that only has the female part is called ___pistillate___.

13. Both of these kinds of flowers are considered ___incomplete___.

14. Instead of flowers, conifers produce seeds by means of ___cones___.

15. The process in which pollen is transferred from an anther to a stigma: ___pollination___

16. The sweet-tasting watery liquid produced by some flowers: ___nectar___

17. Pollination that occurs by the help of a living thing: ___biotic___

18. Pollination that occurs without the help of a living thing: ___abiotic___

19. The uniting of a sperm cell with an egg cell is called ___fertilization___.

20. What is the botanical definition of a fruit? ___A fruit is a seed-bearing structure that results from the fully developed ovary of the flower of a plant.___

21. What does "culinary" mean? ___"having to do with the kitchen"___

22. What is the culinary definition of a fruit? ___A "kitchen fruit" is a seed-bearing structure that is sweet in taste and fleshy in composition.___

23. What are the three categories of fruit? ___simple fruits, aggregate fruits, and multiple fruits___

24. Fruit that grows from a single flower with a single pistil: ___simple___

25. What are the two types of simple fruit? ___fleshy and dry___

26. A simple fruit that is fleshy and juicy throughout: _____berry_____

27. A simple fruit that is fleshy with a woody stone in the center: _____drupe_____

28. A simple fruit that is fleshy with a papery inside layer:_____pome_____

29. An apple is formed from the entire _____receptacle_____ of the flower.

30. What are the five varieties of dry fruits? ___legumes, samaras, nuts, achenes, and grains___

31. A simple dry fruit that consists of a woody or herbaceous pod enclosing several seeds:

_____legume_____

32. A seed with a papery wing that causes it to spin away from the tree:_____samara_____

33. A simple dry fruit in which the seed is enclosed by a thick shell: _____nut_____

34. A simple dry fruit with a thin shell that is mistaken for the nut: _____achene_____

35. A simple dry fruit that comes from grass and has a thin shell that is attached to the seed:

_____grain_____

36. The process of separating grain seeds from their shells is called _____milling_____.

37. A cluster of individual fruit structures grown from the same flower:___aggregate fruit_____

38. A compound fruit that develops from a cluster of individual flowers: ___multiple fruit_____

Diagrams and Labeling

- Label the parts of a flower.

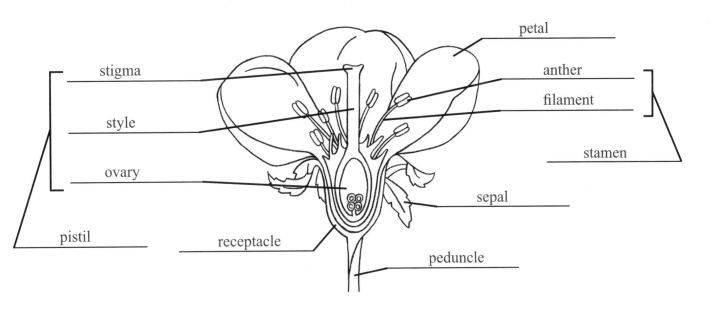

- Label the types of flowers.

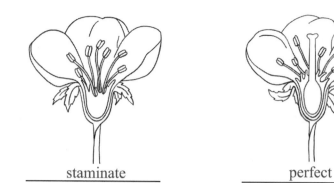

_____ staminate

_____ perfect

_____ pistillate

- Label the male and female cones.

_____ female _____

_____ male _____

- Label the parts of a flower during fertilization.

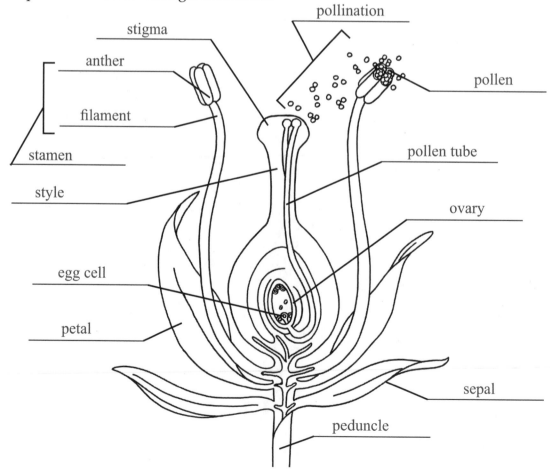

stigma

anther

filament

stamen

style

egg cell

petal

pollination

pollen

pollen tube

ovary

sepal

peduncle

- Label the following fruits according to whether they are fleshy or dry; simple, aggregate, or multiple; what type of simple fleshy or simple dry fruit; and whether they are considered culinary fruits, vegetables, grains, or nuts.

1. rice _____ dry; simple; grain; culinary grain

2. apple _____ fleshy; simple; pome; culinary fruit

3. pineapple _____ fleshy; multiple fruit; culinary fruit

4. sunflower seed _____ dry; simple; achene; culinary nut

5. cucumber _____ fleshy; simple; berry; culinary vegetable

6. peanut _____ dry; simple; legume; culinary nut

7. walnut _____ fleshy; simple; drupe; culinary nut

8. ash tree seed _____ dry; simple; samara; not used in cooking

9. acorn _____ dry; simple; nut; culinary nut

10. tomato _____ fleshy; simple; berry; culinary vegetable

11. barley _____ dry; simple; grain; culinary grain

12. raspberry _____ fleshy; aggregate; culinary fruit

13. green bean _____ dry; simple; legume; culinary vegetable

14. pumpkin _____ fleshy; simple; berry; culinary vegetable

15. peach _____ fleshy; simple; drupe; culinary fruit

16. olive _____ fleshy; simple; drupe; culinary vegetable

17. kiwi _____ fleshy; simple; berry; culinary fruit

18. bell pepper _____ fleshy; simple; berry; culinary vegetable

19. dandelion seed _____ dry; simple; achene; not used in cooking (sometimes tea or medicine)

20. pear _____ fleshy; simple; pome; culinary fruit

* The examples given on the answer layer in the Tree Observations are based on trees found in the immediate vicinity of the HLS Crescent Hill location. Although these trees may not represent what is present in your area, these will at least provide an example as to how to fill in answers on the observation pages.

UNIT IV
Observing Trees

Lesson 15: Observing Trees

Reading and Questions

The Book of Trees pp. 59-63

1. What two characteristics do all trees possess?   <u>All trees are woody plants and have a primary stem.</u>

2. What makes up the crown of a tree? <u>The crown of a tree is all of its aboveground parts: the stem, branches, and leaves.</u>

3. List the seven basic crown shapes.   <u>The seven basic crown shapes are columnar, oval, rounded (or round), vase-shaped, pyramidal, spreading, and weeping.</u>

4. What type of trees are small and used for decoration? _____
   <u>Decorative trees are called ornamental trees.</u>

5. What is a tree's natural habitat? <u>A tree's natural habitat is the type of location and climate in which a tree is most commonly found.</u>

6. What type of tree "outgrows" its bark? <u>sycamore</u>

7. What is the name of the California redwood that currently holds the record as the tallest tree in the world? <u>Hyperion</u> How tall is it? <u>379 ft.</u>

8. Why is the largest Montezuma cypress called the "Tree of Life"? <u>It is called the "Tree of Life" because the large knots in its trunk look like animals stuck in the tree.</u>

Diagrams and Labeling

- Label the images of trees below according to their crown shape.

spreading

weeping

rounded

oval

pyramidal

columnar

vase-shaped

Activities

1. Take a walk outside and try to identify the crown shapes of any trees you encounter.
2. Devise a way to measure the height of a tree.

Tree Observation #1

Observing the Tree

Choose a tree to observe, and collect specimens of leaves, flowers, and fruit.

Structure and Location

- Where is the tree located? _CHBC: near Birchwood lobby, along Birchwood_

- What shape is its crown? (columnar, oval, round, vase-shaped, pyramidal, spreading, or weeping)____pyramidal____ Approximately how tall is it? _30-35 ft._

Bark

- What is the color and texture of the bark? (smooth, fissured, scaly, warty, or combination)
  The bark is greenish gray and mostly smooth, only slightly fissured.

- Does the tree appear to be young or old? Why? _The smooth bark suggests that it is young._

Leaves

- Which of the two major categories of leaves does the tree possess? (broadleaf or needle-leaf)
  The leaf is a broadleaf.

- Does the tree appear to be deciduous or evergreen? ____deciduous____

- What is the texture of the leaf? (smooth, rough, fuzzy, hairy, or waxy) _____
  a little fuzzy

- What is its shape? (linear, oblong, ovate, lanceolate, elliptical, cordate, deltoid, or spatulate)
  The shape is cordate with an uneven base.

- What is the leaf arrangement? (alternate, opposite, or whorled) ____alternate____

- What is the leaf's venation? (pinnate or palmate) ____It is pinnately veined.____

- What is the nature of the leaf margin? (entire, toothed, lobed, or some combination)
  The margin is sharply toothed.

- Are the leaves single or compound? ____single____

- Is there anything special about this leaf? _____

Flowers (If there are no flowers present, fill in this section after referencing the *Peterson Guide* or *The Tree Book*.)

- Does the tree produce flowers or cones? ____flowers____
- What size are the blooms? (large or small) ____small, round____
- What color are the petals? ____pale yellow____

- Is the flower fragrant? _____very fragrant_____
- What type of flower is it? (staminate, pistillate, or perfect) ___perfect___
- Is there anything special about this tree's flowers?_____
  The small flowers grow from a bladelike leaf called a bract.
  _____

Fruits (If there is no fruit present, fill in this section after referencing the *Peterson Guide* or *The Tree Book*.)

- Is the fruit fleshy or dry?___dry___
- Is the fruit simple, aggregate, or multiple? ___simple___
- If a fleshy, simple fruit, what kind is it? (berry, drupe, or pome) _____
- If a dry, simple fruit, what kind is it? (legume, samara, nut, or achene) ___nut___
- Describe it. ___It is a small nutlet covered in small hairs that contains three seeds.___

Identifying the Tree

Using the observations you have made, find the tree in the *Peterson Guide*.

- Common name for this type of tree: ___American Basswood or American Linden___

Researching the Tree

Using the *Peterson Guide* and *The Tree Book*, we can learn more about this type of tree.

- What is the Latin name for this type of tree?___Tilia americana___
- From what Latin words is this name derived?___**tilia, -ae** f. *linden tree*___
  americanus, -a, -um *American*
- What is this type of tree's natural habitat? ___It seems to grow almost anywhere in America.___
  *Not specified in *The Tree Book* or *Peterson Guide*.
- What is the average height of this type of tree?___50-80 ft.___
- What type of wood does this tree have, and for what is it used? _____
  The wood is somewhat soft and easy to carve. Because the wood has no odor or taste, the wood is
  used to make food containers.
  _____

- Share any interesting facts or stories associated with this type of tree._____
  Native Americans would carve masks out of the trunk of the Basswood. The stringy inner bark was
  also used to make rope.
  _____
  _____
  _____
  _____

Sketching

- Common name of the tree: _____
- In the space below, use the leaf sample you collected from the tree you observed, and, to the best of your ability, sketch a picture of the leaf.

Leaf

- In the space below, use the flower or fruit samples you collected, and, to the best of your ability, sketch a picture of each. If you were unable to collect a sample, use a picture in either the *Peterson Guide* or *The Tree Book*.

Flower	**Fruit**

Tree Observation #2

Observing the Tree

Choose a tree to observe, and collect specimens of leaves, flowers, and fruit.

Structure and Location

- Where is the tree located? _CHBC: near Birchwood lobby, along Birchwood_

- What shape is its crown? (columnar, oval, round, vase-shaped, pyramidal, spreading, or weeping) _oval_ Approximately how tall is it? _70-80 ft._

Bark

- What is the color and texture of the bark? (smooth, fissured, scaly, warty, or combination)
  The bark is greenish gray with fissures.

- Does the tree appear to be young or old? Why? _The size and the deepness of the fissures in the bark suggests that it is old._

Leaves

- Which of the two major categories of leaves does the tree possess? (broadleaf or needle-leaf)
  The leaf is a broadleaf.

- Does the tree appear to be deciduous or evergreen? _deciduous_

- What is the texture of the leaf? (smooth, rough, fuzzy, hairy, or waxy) _smooth/glossy_

- What is its shape? (linear, oblong, ovate, lanceolate, elliptical, cordate, deltoid, or spatulate)
  The shape is oval or oblong (large lobes make it hard to see the general shape).

- What is the leaf arrangement? (alternate, opposite, or whorled) _alternate_

- What is the leaf's venation? (pinnate or palmate) _It is pinnately veined._

- What is the nature of the leaf margin? (entire, toothed, lobed, or some combination)
  The margin has large lobes (5) and is slightly toothed.

- Are the leaves single or compound? _single_

- Is there anything special about this leaf? ___

Flowers (If there are no flowers present, fill in this section after referencing the *Peterson Guide* or *The Tree Book*.)

- Does the tree produce flowers or cones? _flowers: male & female_

- What size are the blooms? (large or small) _male flowers are long catkins, females are small_

- What color are the petals? _males: greenish yellow   females: red and green_

- Is the flower fragrant? _____It is rather mild, but males produce a lot of pollen.____
- What type of flower is it? (staminate, pistillate, or perfect) _____has both pistillate and staminate____
- Is there anything special about this tree's flowers?_____Male flowers grow in long catkins. Femal[e] flowers are very inconspicuous and grow at the base of new leaves.____

Fruits (If there is no fruit present, fill in this section after referencing the *Peterson Guide* or *The Tree Book*.)

- Is the fruit fleshy or dry?_____dry____
- Is the fruit simple, aggregate, or multiple? _____simple____
- If a fleshy, simple fruit, what kind is it? (berry, drupe, or pome) _____
- If a dry, simple fruit, what kind is it? (legume, samara, nut, or achene) _____nut____
- Describe it. _____The nut is small and held in a bowl-shaped cup called an acorn. It contains one seed.____

Identifying the Tree

Using the observations you have made, find the tree in the *Peterson Guide*.
- Common name for this type of tree: _____Pin Oak, Red Oak____

Researching the Tree

Using the *Peterson Guide* and *The Tree Book*, we can learn more about this type of tree.
- What is the Latin name for this type of tree?_____Quercus palustris____
- From what Latin words is this name derived?_____**quercus, -i** f. *oak (beautiful tree)*____
  _____**paluster, palustris, palustre** *marshy, fenny*____
- What is this type of tree's natural habitat? _____Grows in areas with a lot of water, poorly drained____

- What is the average height of this type of tree?_____50-80 ft.____
- What type of wood does this tree have, and for what is it used? _____
  _____Oaks in general have heavy, strong wood, used for building furniture and as flooring. Oak is____
  _____waterproof and was used for building ships. It is also used for making barrels.____
  _____*Pin oak wood is uncharacteristically soft and not as valuable as normal oak wood.____
- Share any interesting facts or stories associated with this type of tree._____
  _____Many oaks grow as a result of squirrels burying the nuts to eat during the winter and forgetting them____

Sketching

- Common name of the tree: _____
- In the space below, use the leaf sample you collected from the tree you observed, and, to the best of your ability, sketch a picture of the leaf.

Leaf

- In the space below, use the flower or fruit samples you collected, and, to the best of your ability, sketch a picture of each. If you were unable to collect a sample, use a picture in either the *Peterson Guide* or *The Tree Book.*

Flower

Fruit

Tree Observation #3

Observing the Tree

Choose a tree to observe, and collect specimens of leaves, flowers, and fruit.

Structure and Location

- Where is the tree located? __CHBC: across the street from Birchwood lobby__
- What shape is its crown? (columnar, oval, round, vase-shaped, pyramidal, spreading, or weeping) ___oval/rounded___ Approximately how tall is it? __85-95 ft.__

Bark

- What is the color and texture of the bark? (smooth, fissured, scaly, warty, or combination)
  The bark is grayish brown and scaly.

- Does the tree appear to be young or old? Why? __The really scaly bark and extreme height__ suggests that it is an older tree.

Leaves

- Which of the two major categories of leaves does the tree possess? (broadleaf or needle-leaf)
  The leaf is a broadleaf.
- Does the tree appear to be deciduous or evergreen? ___deciduous___
- What is the texture of the leaf? (smooth, rough, fuzzy, hairy, or waxy) _____
  It is mostly smooth, slightly waxy on top.
- What is its shape? (linear, oblong, ovate, lanceolate, elliptical, cordate, deltoid, or spatulate)
  The shape doesn't really fit our list. It has the shape characteristic of maple leaves.
- What is the leaf arrangement? (alternate, opposite, or whorled) ___opposite___
- What is the leaf's venation? (pinnate or palmate) ___It is palmately veined.___
- What is the nature of the leaf margin? (entire, toothed, lobed, or some combination)
  The margin has five characteristic lobes.
- Are the leaves single or compound? ___single___
- Is there anything special about this leaf? __In the fall, maple leaves change into brilliant shades of__ yellow, gold, and red.

Flowers (If there are no flowers present, fill in this section after referencing the *Peterson Guide* or *The Tree Book*.)

- Does the tree produce flowers or cones? ___flowers___
- What size are the blooms? (large or small) ___long with small blooms___
- What color are the petals? ___greenish yellow___

- Is the flower fragrant? _____subtle_____
- What type of flower is it? (staminate, pistillate, or perfect) ____has both staminate and pistillate_
- Is there anything special about this tree's flowers?_____
  The maple has so many flowers it can sometimes appear yellow in color.

Fruits (If there is no fruit present, fill in this section after referencing the *Peterson Guide* or *The Tree Book*.)

- Is the fruit fleshy or dry?___dry_____
- Is the fruit simple, aggregate, or multiple? _____simple_____
- If a fleshy, simple fruit, what kind is it? (berry, drupe, or pome) _____
- If a dry, simple fruit, what kind is it? (legume, samara, nut, or achene) ____samara____
- Describe it. ___Each wing contains one seed and acts like a helicopter, transporting the seed to a__
  new location.

Identifying the Tree

Using the observations you have made, find the tree in the *Peterson Guide*.

- Common name for this type of tree: _____Sugar Maple_____

Researching the Tree

Using the *Peterson Guide* and *The Tree Book*, we can learn more about this type of tree.

- What is the Latin name for this type of tree?____Acer saccharum_____
- From what Latin words is this name derived?___**acer, aceris** n. *maple tree*_____
  _____**saccharus, -a, -um** *cane sugar*_____
- What is this type of tree's natural habitat? _____Grows in eastern North America_____

- What is the average height of this type of tree?_____60-100 ft._____
- What type of wood does this tree have, and for what is it used? _____
  The wood is hard and can have wavy growth rings or irregularities in the growth rings which make
  beautiful, highly figured wood for cabinets and furniture. The wood is also so hard that it is used for
  bowling alley floors.
- Share any interesting facts or stories associated with this type of tree._____
  The sugar maple is known for its particularly sweet sap. Maple trees used to be tapped by boring a
  hole in the trunk and placing a spout in the hole. It takes 40 gallons of sap to make 1 gallon of syrup.

Sketching

- Common name of the tree: _____
- In the space below, use the leaf sample you collected from the tree you observed, and, to the best of your ability, sketch a picture of the leaf.

Leaf

- In the space below, use the flower or fruit samples you collected, and, to the best of your ability, sketch a picture of each. If you were unable to collect a sample, use a picture in either the *Peterson Guide* or *The Tree Book*.

Flower	**Fruit**

Observing the Tree

Choose a tree to observe, and collect specimens of leaves, flowers, and fruit.

Structure and Location

- Where is the tree located? __CHBC: alley at south end of building (by fellowship hall)__
- What shape is its crown? (columnar, oval, round, vase-shaped, pyramidal, spreading, or weeping)____vase-shaped____ Approximately how tall is it? __40-50 ft.__

Bark

- What is the color and texture of the bark? (smooth, fissured, scaly, warty, or combination)
  __The bark is brownish gray with deep vertical fissures.__

- Does the tree appear to be young or old? Why? __Its size suggests that it isn't very old.__

Leaves

- Which of the two major categories of leaves does the tree possess? (broadleaf or needle-leaf)
  __The leaf is a broadleaf.__
- Does the tree appear to be deciduous or evergreen? ____deciduous____
- What is the texture of the leaf? (smooth, rough, fuzzy, hairy, or waxy) _____
  __It has a smooth top and a soft, hairy bottom.__
- What is its shape? (linear, oblong, ovate, lanceolate, elliptical, cordate, deltoid, or spatulate)
  __The shape is ovate with an uneven base.__
- What is the leaf arrangement? (alternate, opposite, or whorled) ____alternate____
- What is the leaf's venation? (pinnate or palmate) ____It is pinnately veined.____
- What is the nature of the leaf margin? (entire, toothed, lobed, or some combination)
  __The margin is double-toothed.__
- Are the leaves single or compound? ____single____
- Is there anything special about this leaf? __Besides being double-toothed, elm leaves turn yellow in the fall.__

Flowers (If there are no flowers present, fill in this section after referencing the *Peterson Guide* or *The Tree Book*.)

- Does the tree produce flowers or cones?____flowers____
- What size are the blooms? (large or small)____clusters of small hanging blooms____
- What color are the petals?____reddish purple and green____

- Is the flower fragrant? _____ not very fragrant
- What type of flower is it? (staminate, pistillate, or perfect) ____ perfect
- Is there anything special about this tree's flowers?____
  The flowers on an elm actually show up before the leaves in spring.

Fruits (If there is no fruit present, fill in this section after referencing the *Peterson Guide* or *The Tree Book*.)
- Is the fruit fleshy or dry?____ dry
- Is the fruit simple, aggregate, or multiple? ____ simple
- If a fleshy, simple fruit, what kind is it? (berry, drupe, or pome) ____
- If a dry, simple fruit, what kind is it? (legume, samara, nut, or achene) ____ samara
- Describe it. ____ The samara has one flat, disc-shaped wing that houses one seed. It is greenish brown
  with hairs on the edges.

Identifying the Tree

Using the observations you have made, find the tree in the *Peterson Guide*.
- Common name for this type of tree: ____ American Elm

Researching the Tree

Using the *Peterson Guide* and *The Tree Book*, we can learn more about this type of tree.
- What is the Latin name for this type of tree?____ Ulmus americana
- From what Latin words is this name derived?____ **ulmus, -i** f. *elm tree*
  Americanus, -a, -um *American*
- What is this type of tree's natural habitat? ____ It grows in eastern North America and is
  frequently planted throughout eastern towns.
- What is the average height of this type of tree?____ 60-80 ft.
- What type of wood does this tree have, and for what is it used? ____
  Elm wood has interlaced fibers that make it tough to split. It was eventually used for making
  automobile parts, particularly wheel hubs.

- Share any interesting facts or stories associated with this type of tree.____
  Elms are usually planted on opposite sides of a road because they form arches over it. However, a
  majority of elms have died due to Dutch elm disease. The disease was spread by infected beetles tha
  came in a shipment of wood from Asia.

Sketching

- Common name of the tree: _____
- In the space below, use the leaf sample you collected from the tree you observed, and, to the best of your ability, sketch a picture of the leaf.

Leaf

- In the space below, use the flower or fruit samples you collected, and, to the best of your ability, sketch a picture of each. If you were unable to collect a sample, use a picture in either the *Peterson Guide* or *The Tree Book*.

Flower	**Fruit**

Observing the Tree

Choose a tree to observe, and collect specimens of leaves, flowers, and fruit.

Structure and Location

- Where is the tree located? __CHBC: back alley near "secret garden" in St. Mark's__

- What shape is its crown? (columnar, oval, round, vase-shaped, pyramidal, spreading, or weeping)____round/spreading____ Approximately how tall is it? __45-55 ft.__

Bark

- What is the color and texture of the bark? (smooth, fissured, scaly, warty, or combination)
  __The bark is dark gray with deep fissures.__

- Does the tree appear to be young or old? Why? __It is not particularly tall, but the bark is fissured.__
  __It is perhaps an older tree that didn't have room to grow.__

Leaves

- Which of the two major categories of leaves does the tree possess? (broadleaf or needle-leaf)
  __The leaf is a broadleaf.__

- Does the tree appear to be deciduous or evergreen? ____deciduous____

- What is the texture of the leaf? (smooth, rough, fuzzy, hairy, or waxy) _____
  __It is mostly smooth, slightly fuzzy.__

- What is its shape? (linear, oblong, ovate, lanceolate, elliptic, cordate, deltoid, or spatulate)
  __The leaflet shape is oval/ovate.__

- What is the leaf arrangement? (alternate, opposite, or whorled) ____alternate____

- What is the leaf's venation? (pinnate or palmate) ____It is pinnately veined.____

- What is the nature of the leaf margin? (entire, toothed, lobed, or some combination)
  __The leaflet margins are toothed.__

- Are the leaves single or compound? ____pinnately compound____

- Is there anything special about this leaf? __Leaves can grow to almost 2' in length. They also have a__
  __pleasing, spicy smell when ground.__

Flowers (If there are no flowers present, fill in this section after referencing the *Peterson Guide* or *The Tree Book*.)

- Does the tree produce flowers or cones?____flowers____

- What size are the blooms? (large or small)____male: long catkins; female: small blooms____

- What color are the petals?____male: greenish yellow; female: red and green____

- Is the flower fragrant? _____The flowers are less fragrant than the leaves._____
- What type of flower is it? (staminate, pistillate, or perfect) _____has both staminate and pistillate_____
- Is there anything special about this tree's flowers?_____
  The male flowers are catkins that aren't particularly large. The pistils of the female flower are very large for the size of the flower, in order to collect more pollen.

Fruits (If there is no fruit present, fill in this section after referencing the *Peterson Guide* or *The Tree Book*.)

- Is the fruit fleshy or dry?_____dry_____
- Is the fruit simple, aggregate, or multiple? _____simple_____
- If a fleshy, simple fruit, what kind is it? (berry, drupe, or pome) _____
- If a dry, simple fruit, what kind is it? (legume, samara, nut, or achene) _____nut_____
- Describe it. _____The nut is fit inside a hard, bony shell with a thick green husk around it. The walnut is used in cooking, but the husk stains anything with which it comes into contact._____

Identifying the Tree

Using the observations you have made, find the tree in the *Peterson Guide*.

- Common name for this type of tree: _____Black Walnut_____

Researching the Tree

Using the *Peterson Guide* and *The Tree Book*, we can learn more about this type of tree.

- What is the Latin name for this type of tree?_____Juglans nigra_____
- From what Latin words is this name derived?_____**juglans, juglandis** f. *walnut tree*_____
  niger, nigra, nigrum *black*
- What is this type of tree's natural habitat? _____grows in eastern North America_____
- What is the average height of this type of tree?_____70-90 ft._____
- What type of wood does this tree have, and for what is it used? _____
  The wood is beautiful and extremely valuable. It is used for furniture and floors.
- Share any interesting facts or stories associated with this type of tree._____
  Walnut trees are the first to lose their leaves in the fall. The tough shell that encases the nut is used to clean and polish metal, including jet engines.

Sketching

- Common name of the tree: _____
- In the space below, use the leaf sample you collected from the tree you observed, and, to the best of your ability, sketch a picture of the leaf.

Leaf

- In the space below, use the flower or fruit samples you collected, and, to the best of your ability, sketch a picture of each. If you were unable to collect a sample, use a picture in either the *Peterson Guide* or *The Tree Book*.

Flower	**Fruit**

Observing the Tree

Choose a tree to observe, and collect specimens of leaves, flowers, and fruit.

Structure and Location

- Where is the tree located? _CHBC: back alley near "secret garden" in St. Mark's_
- What shape is its crown? (columnar, oval, round, vase-shaped, pyramidal, spreading, or weeping)_____spreading_____ Approximately how tall is it? _20-30 ft._

Bark

- What is the color and texture of the bark? (smooth, fissured, scaly, warty, or combination)
  The bark is grayish brown and scaly.

- Does the tree appear to be young or old? Why? _small tree but has scaly/fissured bark; seems to be a mature tree_

Leaves

- Which of the two major categories of leaves does the tree possess? (broadleaf or needle-leaf)
  The leaf is a broadleaf.
- Does the tree appear to be deciduous or evergreen? _____deciduous_____
- What is the texture of the leaf? (smooth, rough, fuzzy, hairy, or waxy) _____
  It is rough on top and hairy on bottom.
- What is its shape? (linear, oblong, ovate, lanceolate, elliptical, cordate, deltoid, or spatulate)
  The leaflets are cordate.
- What is the leaf arrangement? (alternate, opposite, or whorled) _____alternate_____
- What is the leaf's venation? (pinnate or palmate) _____some pinnate and some palmate_____
- What is the nature of the leaf margin? (entire, toothed, lobed, or some combination)
  The leaves are finely toothed. Some of the leaves are lobed.
- Are the leaves single or compound? _____single_____
- Is there anything special about this leaf? _The leaves can vary in shape. Some have a mitten shape._

Flowers (If there are no flowers present, fill in this section after referencing the *Peterson Guide* or *The Tree Book*.)

- Does the tree produce flowers or cones?_____flowers_____
- What size are the blooms? (large or small)_____tiny blooms_____
- What color are the petals?_____yellowish green_____

- Is the flower fragrant? _____ not noticeable _____
- What type of flower is it? (staminate, pistillate, or perfect) _has both staminate and pistillate_
- Is there anything special about this tree's flowers? _____ The tiny cup-shaped flowers occur in clusters. Male flowers and female flowers are often on separate trees but can occur on the same tree.

Fruits (If there is no fruit present, fill in this section after referencing the *Peterson Guide* or *The Tree Book*.)
- Is the fruit fleshy or dry? _____ fleshy
- Is the fruit simple, aggregate, or multiple? _____ aggregate
- If a fleshy, simple fruit, what kind is it? (berry, drupe, or pome) _____
- If a dry, simple fruit, what kind is it? (legume, samara, nut, or achene) _____
- Describe it. _____ 1-inch long edible red berries that turn purple when ripe in the summer

Identifying the Tree

Using the observations you have made, find the tree in the *Peterson Guide*.
- Common name for this type of tree: _____ Red Mulberry

Researching the Tree

Using the *Peterson Guide* and *The Tree Book*, we can learn more about this type of tree.
- What is the Latin name for this type of tree? _____ Morus rubra
- From what Latin words is this name derived? _____ **morus, i** f.   *mulberry*

  ruber, rubra, rubrum   *red*
- What is this type of tree's natural habitat? _____ native to eastern U.S.; can endure harsh weather rather well
- What is the average height of this type of tree? _____ 25-50 ft.
- What type of wood does this tree have, and for what is it used? _____

  The wood is not usually used. However, Choctaw women made cloaks from the bark by drying, beating, bleaching, spinning, and weaving the strong fibers. The stringy bark was also used to make ropes by early explorers.
- Share any interesting facts or stories associated with this type of tree. _____

  Silkworms feed on the white mulberry, Morus alba, of Asia, which was imported to America after early settlers discovered that the silkworm would not grow on the red mulberry. In some states the white mulberry is more common than the native red, but not in KY. The white mulberry is a smaller tree, with a smaller fruit. Its leaves are smooth on top and glabrous (no hairs) except on veins beneath. There is a white mulberry next to the bamboo stand at the end of the alley.

Sketching

- Common name of the tree: _____
- In the space below, use the leaf sample you collected from the tree you observed, and, to the best of your ability, sketch a picture of the leaf.

Leaf

- In the space below, use the flower or fruit samples you collected, and, to the best of your ability, sketch a picture of each. If you were unable to collect a sample, use a picture in either the *Peterson Guide* or *The Tree Book*.

Flower	Fruit

Observing the Tree

Choose a tree to observe, and collect specimens of leaves, flowers, and fruit.

Structure and Location

- Where is the tree located? __CHBC: on Frankfort on the west side of St. Mark's__
- What shape is its crown? (columnar, oval, round, vase-shaped, pyramidal, spreading, or weeping)____pyramidal____ Approximately how tall is it? __25-30 ft.__

Bark

- What is the color and texture of the bark? (smooth, fissured, scaly, warty, or combination)
  __The bark is greenish brown with some slight fissures.__

- Does the tree appear to be young or old? Why? __neither tall nor fissured; seems relatively young__

Leaves

- Which of the two major categories of leaves does the tree possess? (broadleaf or needle-leaf)
  __The leaf is a needle-leaf.__
- Does the tree appear to be deciduous or evergreen? ____evergreen____
- What is the texture of the leaf? (smooth, rough, fuzzy, hairy, or waxy) _____
  __It is mostly smooth.__
- What is its shape? (linear, oblong, ovate, lanceolate, elliptical, cordate, deltoid, or spatulate)
  __N/A__
- What is the leaf arrangement? (alternate, opposite, or whorled) ____N/A____
- What is the leaf's venation? (pinnate or palmate) ____N/A____
- What is the nature of the leaf margin? (entire, toothed, lobed, or some combination)
  __N/A__
- Are the leaves single or compound? ____N/A____
- Is there anything special about this leaf? __Needles grow in bundles of five called fascicles. Each__
  __needle has a thin, white stripe.__

Flowers (If there are no flowers present, fill in this section after referencing the *Peterson Guide* or *The Tree Book*.)

- Does the tree produce flowers or cones?____cones____
- What size are the blooms? (large or small)__male: small pollen cones; female: large, long cones__
- What color are the petals?____male: yellow; female: start pink and become brown__

- Is the flower fragrant? _____No, but the pine needles are very fragrant._____
- What type of flower is it? (staminate, pistillate, or perfect) _____N/A_____
- Is there anything special about this tree's flowers?_____

  It has both male and female cones on the same tree._____

  _____

Fruits (If there is no fruit present, fill in this section after referencing the *Peterson Guide* or *The Tree Book*.)
- Is the fruit fleshy or dry?_____dry_____
- Is the fruit simple, aggregate, or multiple? _____N/A_____
- If a fleshy, simple fruit, what kind is it? (berry, drupe, or pome) _____
- If a dry, simple fruit, what kind is it? (legume, samara, nut, or achene) _____
- Describe it. _____The White Pine has cones with produce seeds with papery wings._____

  _____

Identifying the Tree

Using the observations you have made, find the tree in the *Peterson Guide*.
- Common name for this type of tree: _____White Pine_____

Researching the Tree

Using the *Peterson Guide* and *The Tree Book*, we can learn more about this type of tree.
- What is the Latin name for this type of tree?_____Pinus strobus_____
- From what Latin words is this name derived?_____**pinus, pinus** f. *pine*_____

  _____**strobus, -is** m. *cone*_____
- What is this type of tree's natural habitat? _____grows in eastern North America_____

  _____
- What is the average height of this type of tree?_____80-150 ft._____
- What type of wood does this tree have, and for what is it used? _____

  The wood is soft but strong. It is easily worked, and since it grows so straight, it was used for

  making masts for ships._____

  _____
- Share any interesting facts or stories associated with this type of tree._____

  To the Native Americans, the grouping of five needles represented the Five Nations (tribes in

  northeastern America which had joined together). The white pine became a symbol of peace for the

  Native Americans of those tribes._____

  _____

  _____

  _____

Sketching

- Common name of the tree: _____
- In the space below, use the leaf sample you collected from the tree you observed, and, to the best of your ability, sketch a picture of the leaf.

Leaf

- In the space below, use the flower or fruit samples you collected, and, to the best of your ability, sketch a picture of each. If you were unable to collect a sample, use a picture in either the *Peterson Guide* or *The Tree Book*.

Flower | **Fruit**

Observing the Tree

Choose a tree to observe, and collect specimens of leaves, flowers, and fruit.

Structure and Location

- Where is the tree located? _CHBC: front lawn of St. Mark's, left of red doors_
- What shape is its crown? (columnar, oval, round, vase-shaped, pyramidal, spreading, or weeping) _spreading_ Approximately how tall is it? _10-15 ft._

Bark

- What is the color and texture of the bark? (smooth, fissured, scaly, warty, or combination)
  The bark is gray with square-shaped fissures that make it appear "checkered."

- Does the tree appear to be young or old? Why? _short, but has rather checkered bark; neither really old nor very young_

Leaves

- Which of the two major categories of leaves does the tree possess? (broadleaf or needle-leaf)
  The leaf is a broadleaf.
- Does the tree appear to be deciduous or evergreen? _deciduous_
- What is the texture of the leaf? (smooth, rough, fuzzy, hairy, or waxy) _____
  It is mostly smooth and glossy.
- What is its shape? (linear, oblong, ovate, lanceolate, elliptical, cordate, deltoid, or spatulate)
  ovate
- What is the leaf arrangement? (alternate, opposite, or whorled) _opposite_
- What is the leaf's venation? (pinnate or palmate) _palmate_
- What is the nature of the leaf margin? (entire, toothed, lobed, or some combination)
  entire
- Are the leaves single or compound? _single_
- Is there anything special about this leaf? _In the fall, the leaf turns a bright, purple-ish red._

Flowers (If there are no flowers present, fill in this section after referencing the *Peterson Guide* or *The Tree Book*.)

- Does the tree produce flowers or cones? _flowers_
- What size are the blooms? (large or small) _small_
- What color are the petals? _yellow and green clusters_

- Is the flower fragrant? _____ strong, pleasing smell
- What type of flower is it? (staminate, pistillate, or perfect) ____ perfect
- Is there anything special about this tree's flowers? _Each bloom has a cluster of around 20 flowers_ in the center. The white, pink-edged parts that look like petals are actually bracts (specialized leaves)

Fruits (If there is no fruit present, fill in this section after referencing the *Peterson Guide* or *The Tree Book*.)
- Is the fruit fleshy or dry?____ fleshy
- Is the fruit simple, aggregate, or multiple? _____ simple
- If a fleshy, simple fruit, what kind is it? (berry, drupe, or pome) _____ drupe
- If a dry, simple fruit, what kind is it? (legume, samara, nut, or achene) _____
- Describe it. ___The drupe is bright red and football-shaped. It is a favorite of birds.

Identifying the Tree

Using the observations you have made, find the tree in the *Peterson Guide*.
- Common name for this type of tree: _____ Flowering Dogwood

Researching the Tree

Using the *Peterson Guide* and *The Tree Book*, we can learn more about this type of tree.
- What is the Latin name for this type of tree?____ Cornus florida
- From what Latin words is this name derived?____ **cornus, -i** f. *cornel tree*
  floridus, -a, -um *flowery*
- What is this type of tree's natural habitat? _____ grows in shady, wet areas in eastern U.S.

- What is the average height of this type of tree?_____ 20-30 ft.
- What type of wood does this tree have, and for what is it used? _____
  The wood is hard and tough. It is used for tool handles and it used to be used for golf club heads.
  The Native Americans used the bark and roots to cure malaria. The ends of branches were also used
  as toothbrushes.
- Share any interesting facts or stories associated with this type of tree._____
  The dogwood got its name from the use of its wood, not from any animal. The hard wood was used
  for arrows and skewers called "dags" (later "dogs"). Since these dogs would normally come from
  the branches of this tree, it came to be called the dogwood tree.
  In *The Canterbury Tales*, the dogwood is referred to as the "whipple-tree."

Sketching

- Common name of the tree: _____
- In the space below, use the leaf sample you collected from the tree you observed, and, to the best of your ability, sketch a picture of the leaf.

Leaf

- In the space below, use the flower or fruit samples you collected, and, to the best of your ability, sketch a picture of each. If you were unable to collect a sample, use a picture in either the *Peterson Guide* or *The Tree Book*.

Flower	**Fruit**

Observing the Tree

Choose a tree to observe, and collect specimens of leaves, flowers, and fruit.

Structure and Location

- Where is the tree located? ___CHBC: back of St. Mark's parking lot___
- What shape is its crown? (columnar, oval, round, vase-shaped, pyramidal, spreading, or weeping)____spreading_____ Approximately how tall is it? __60-70 ft.__

Bark

- What is the color and texture of the bark? (smooth, fissured, scaly, warty, or combination)
  ___The bark is gray and smooth with patches of yellow, brown, and green.___

- Does the tree appear to be young or old? Why? ___The tree is tall and thick. It seems to be older.___

Leaves

- Which of the two major categories of leaves does the tree possess? (broadleaf or needle-leaf)
  ___The leaf is a broadleaf.___
- Does the tree appear to be deciduous or evergreen? ____deciduous____
- What is the texture of the leaf? (smooth, rough, fuzzy, hairy, or waxy) _____
  ___It is smooth on top and very fuzzy on bottom.___
- What is its shape? (linear, oblong, ovate, lanceolate, elliptical, cordate, deltoid, or spatulate)
  ___ovate; the shape is similar to that of a maple, but much larger and irregular___
- What is the leaf arrangement? (alternate, opposite, or whorled) ____alternate____
- What is the leaf's venation? (pinnate or palmate) ____palmate____
- What is the nature of the leaf margin? (entire, toothed, lobed, or some combination)
  ___large lobes; coarsely toothed___
- Are the leaves single or compound? ____single____
- Is there anything special about this leaf? ___The leaves are quite large. They turn a pale yellow-brown in the fall.___

Flowers (If there are no flowers present, fill in this section after referencing the *Peterson Guide* or *The Tree Book*.)

- Does the tree produce flowers or cones?____flowers____
- What size are the blooms? (large or small)____male smaller than female____
- What color are the petals?____male: green/yellow   female: red and green____

- Is the flower fragrant? _____not strong_____
- What type of flower is it? (staminate, pistillate, or perfect) _has both pistillate and staminate_
- Is there anything special about this tree's flowers? _____The really small flowers grow as ball_ clusters at the end of catkins. The male catkins grow on different branches than the female catkins.

Fruits (If there is no fruit present, fill in this section after referencing the *Peterson Guide* or *The Tree Book*.)

- Is the fruit fleshy or dry? _____dry_____
- Is the fruit simple, aggregate, or multiple? _____simple_____
- If a fleshy, simple fruit, what kind is it? (berry, drupe, or pome) _____
- If a dry, simple fruit, what kind is it? (legume, samara, nut, or achene) _____nut_____
- Describe it. _____The fruit is a ball with many tufted nutlets containing seeds._____

Identifying the Tree

Using the observations you have made, find the tree in the *Peterson Guide*.
- Common name for this type of tree: _____Eastern Sycamore_____

Researching the Tree

Using the *Peterson Guide* and *The Tree Book*, we can learn more about this type of tree.
- What is the Latin name for this type of tree? _____Platanus occidentalis_____
- From what Latin words is this name derived? _____**Platanus, -i** m. *Plane tree*_____ **occidentalis, -e** *of or coming from the West*
- What is this type of tree's natural habitat? _____It can grow in poor soil and air conditions, which makes it a good city tree._____
- What is the average height of this type of tree? _____120-150 ft._____
- What type of wood does this tree have, and for what is it used? _____ The wood is not extremely hard or decay-proof. It is used for chopping blocks because it does not easily split.

- Share any interesting facts or stories associated with this type of tree._____ The outer bark is unable to grow as the tree expands, and peels off in irregular chunks to reveal the white inner bark. The bark becomes whiter from the base of the trunk to the tip. It resembles a soldier's camouflage-patterned uniform.

Sketching

- Common name of the tree: _____
- In the space below, use the leaf sample you collected from the tree you observed, and, to the best of your ability, sketch a picture of the leaf.

Leaf

- In the space below, use the flower or fruit samples you collected, and, to the best of your ability, sketch a picture of each. If you were unable to collect a sample, use a picture in either the *Peterson Guide* or *The Tree Book*.

Flower	**Fruit**

Tree Observation #10

Observing the Tree

Choose a tree to observe, and collect specimens of leaves, flowers, and fruit.

Structure and Location

- Where is the tree located? _____CHBC: in front of building, east of main entrance_____

- What shape is its crown? (columnar, oval, round, vase-shaped, pyramidal, spreading, or weeping)_____spreading_____ Approximately how tall is it? _65-75 ft._

Bark

- What is the color and texture of the bark? (smooth, fissured, scaly, warty, or combination)
  The bark is brownish-gray with deep fissures.

- Does the tree appear to be young or old? Why? __The tree is tall, thick, and fissured. It seems to be older. (It also has blooms, which means it must be at least 15-25 years old.)

Leaves

- Which of the two major categories of leaves does the tree possess? (broadleaf or needle-leaf)
  The leaf is a broadleaf.

- Does the tree appear to be deciduous or evergreen? _____deciduous_____

- What is the texture of the leaf? (smooth, rough, fuzzy, hairy, or waxy) _____
  It is smooth and glossy.

- What is its shape? (linear, oblong, ovate, lanceolate, elliptical, cordate, deltoid, or spatulate)
  The shape doesn't really fit one of our options; it is almost the shape of a saddle.

- What is the leaf arrangement? (alternate, opposite, or whorled) _____alternate_____

- What is the leaf's venation? (pinnate or palmate) _____pinnate_____

- What is the nature of the leaf margin? (entire, toothed, lobed, or some combination)
  It has four symmetrical lobes.

- Are the leaves single or compound? _____single_____

- Is there anything special about this leaf? _____

Flowers (If there are no flowers present, fill in this section after referencing the *Peterson Guide* or *The Tree Book*.)

- Does the tree produce flowers or cones?_____flowers_____

- What size are the blooms? (large or small)_____large_____

- What color are the petals?_____greenish-yellow with orange highlights

- Is the flower fragrant? _____looks like a tulip, but doesn't smell like one_____
- What type of flower is it? (staminate, pistillate, or perfect) _____perfect_____
- Is there anything special about this tree's flowers? _____The flowers don't appear on the tree until it is at least 15-20 years old._____

Fruits (If there is no fruit present, fill in this section after referencing the Peterson Guide or The Tree Book.)
- Is the fruit fleshy or dry? _____dry_____
- Is the fruit simple, aggregate, or multiple? _____simple_____
- If a fleshy, simple fruit, what kind is it? (berry, drupe, or pome) _____
- If a dry, simple fruit, what kind is it? (legume, samara, nut, or achene) _____samara_____
- Describe it. _____The samaras come in a cone-shaped cluster._____

Identifying the Tree

Using the observations you have made, find the tree in the *Peterson Guide*.
- Common name for this type of tree: _____Tulip tree, tulip poplar, or tulip magnolia_____

Researching the Tree

Using the *Peterson Guide* and *The Tree Book*, we can learn more about this type of tree.
- What is the Latin name for this type of tree? _____Liriodendron tulipifera_____
- From what Latin words is this name derived? _____**lirium, -i** n. *lily*_____
  _____**dendron** *tree* (Greek)_____ **fero, ferre** *to bear, carry*
- What is this type of tree's natural habitat? _____eastern U.S.; needs rich soil in order to grow_____
- What is the average height of this type of tree? _____70-90 ft., but can reach close to 200 ft._____
- What type of wood does this tree have, and for what is it used? _____
  The wood is lightweight and soft. It was used by the Native Americans to make canoes. It is used now for house construction.
- Share any interesting facts or stories associated with this type of tree. _____
  It is the tallest hardwood species in the U.S. It is the state tree of Indiana, Tennessee, and Kentucky.

Sketching

- Common name of the tree: _____
- In the space below, use the leaf sample you collected from the tree you observed, and, to the best of your ability, sketch a picture of the leaf.

Leaf

- In the space below, use the flower or fruit samples you collected, and, to the best of your ability, sketch a picture of each. If you were unable to collect a sample, use a picture in either the *Peterson Guide* or *The Tree Book*.

Flower	Fruit

Observing the Tree

* The Hackberry is not found in *The Tree Book*. Have the studer look up the information in an encyclopedia or on the internet, just use this key to supply answers they don't find.

Choose a tree to observe, and collect specimens of leaves, flowers, and fruit.

Structure and Location

- Where is the tree located? __CHBC: in front of building, west of main entrance__

- What shape is its crown? (columnar, oval, round, vase-shaped, pyramidal, spreading, or weeping)___columnar/oval___ Approximately how tall is it? __75-80 ft.__

Bark

- What is the color and texture of the bark? (smooth, fissured, scaly, warty, or combination)
  __The bark is greenish and brownish-gray with large warts.__

- Does the tree appear to be young or old? Why? __The tree is tall, thick, and significantly warty. It seems to be older.__

Leaves

- Which of the two major categories of leaves does the tree possess? (broad-leaf or needle-leaf)
  __The leaf is a broadleaf.__

- Does the tree appear to be deciduous or evergreen? __deciduous__

- What is the texture of the leaf? (smooth, rough, fuzzy, hairy, or waxy) ___
  __It is fuzzy and papery.__

- What is its shape? (linear, oblong, ovate, lanceolate, elliptical, cordate, deltoid, or spatulate)
  __ovate, slightly curved to one side, unsymmetrical and uneven at the base__

- What is the leaf arrangement? (alternate, opposite, or whorled) __alternate__

- What is the leaf's venation? (pinnate or palmate) __pinnate__

- What is the nature of the leaf margin? (entire, toothed, lobed, or some combination)
  __single-toothed__

- Are the leaves single or compound? __single__

- Is there anything special about this leaf? ___

Flowers (If there are no flowers present, fill in this section after referencing the *Peterson Guide* or *The Tree Book*.)

- Does the tree produce flowers or cones?__flowers__

- What size are the blooms? (large or small)__male: long; female: small__

- What color are the petals?__greenish__

- Is the flower fragrant? _____ not very _____
- What type of flower is it? (staminate, pistillate, or perfect) _____ staminate and pistillate _____
- Is there anything special about this tree's flowers? _____ The tiny, inconspicuous flowers bloom in early spring when the leaves are unfolding. Long, fuzzy, male flowers pollinate rounded female flowers on the same branch. _____

Fruits (If there is no fruit present, fill in this section after referencing the *Peterson Guide* or *The Tree Book*.)

- Is the fruit fleshy or dry? _____ fleshy _____
- Is the fruit simple, aggregate, or multiple? _____ simple _____
- If a fleshy, simple fruit, what kind is it? (berry, drupe, or pome) _____ drupe _____
- If a dry, simple fruit, what kind is it? (legume, samara, nut, or achene) _____
- Describe it. _____ The small, round drupe starts out green and then becomes dark red when mature in the fall. _____

Identifying the Tree

Using the observations you have made, find the tree in the *Peterson Guide*.

- Common name for this type of tree: _____ Hackberry, Common Hackberry, or American Hackberry _____

Researching the Tree

Using the *Peterson Guide* and *The Tree Book*, we can learn more about this type of tree.

- What is the Latin name for this type of tree? _____ Celtis occidentalis _____
- From what Latin words is this name derived? _____ **Celtis, -e** *of or pertaining to the Celts*

  occidentalis, -e *of or coming from the West*

- What is this type of tree's natural habitat? _____ eastern U.S.; common in bluegrass region _____

- What is the average height of this type of tree? _____ 70-80 ft. _____
- What type of wood does this tree have, and for what is it used? _____

  Tough, flexible, free-splitting wood that has had rather humble uses, such as tobacco sticks. _____

- Share any interesting facts or stories associated with this type of tree. _____

  Hackberries commonly have a phenomenon called "witches broom." "Witches broom" is a tangle of twigs in a tree crown. _____

Sketching

- Common name of the tree: _____
- In the space below, use the leaf sample you collected from the tree you observed, and, to the best of your ability, sketch a picture of the leaf.

Leaf

- In the space below, use the flower or fruit samples you collected, and, to the best of your ability, sketch a picture of each. If you were unable to collect a sample, use a picture in either the *Peterson Guide* or *The Tree Book*.

Flower	**Fruit**

Observing the Tree

*The American holly is not found in *The Tree Book*. Have the students look up the information in an encyclopedia or on the internet, or just use this key to supply answers they don't find.

Choose a tree to observe, and collect specimens of leaves, flowers, and fruit.

Structure and Location

- Where is the tree located? ___CHBC: in alley leading from Birchwood to library parking lot___

- What shape is its crown? (columnar, oval, round, vase-shaped, pyramidal, spreading, or weeping)___pyramidal___ Approximately how tall is it? ___20-35 ft.___

Bark

- What is the color and texture of the bark? (smooth, fissured, scaly, warty, or combination)
  ___The bark is gray and smooth with some cracking.___

- Does the tree appear to be young or old? Why? ___The tree is tall and the bark is cracked. It seems to be a mature tree.___

Leaves

- Which of the two major categories of leaves does the tree possess? (broadleaf or needle-leaf)
  ___The leaf is a broadleaf.___

- Does the tree appear to be deciduous or evergreen? ___evergreen___

- What is the texture of the leaf? (smooth, rough, fuzzy, hairy, or waxy) ___
  ___It is thick and waxy.___

- What is its shape? (linear, oblong, ovate, lanceolate, elliptical, cordate, deltoid, or spatulate)
  ___oval___

- What is the leaf arrangement? (alternate, opposite, or whorled) ___alternate___

- What is the leaf's venation? (pinnate or palmate) ___pinnate___

- What is the nature of the leaf margin? (entire, toothed, lobed, or some combination)
  ___few large teeth___

- Are the leaves single or compound? ___single___

- Is there anything special about this leaf? ___One of few broadleafs that are also evergreen.___

Flowers (If there are no flowers present, fill in this section after referencing the *Peterson Guide* or *The Tree Book*.)

- Does the tree produce flowers or cones?___flowers___

- What size are the blooms? (large or small)___very small___

- What color are the petals?___white___

- Is the flower fragrant? _____ mildly fragrant
- What type of flower is it? (staminate, pistillate, or perfect) _____ has both staminate and pistillate
- Is there anything special about this tree's flowers? _____ Male holly trees have only staminate flowers, and female trees usually have both staminate and pistillate flowers.

Fruits (If there is no fruit present, fill in this section after referencing the *Peterson Guide* or *The Tree Book*.)
- Is the fruit fleshy or dry? _____ fleshy
- Is the fruit simple, aggregate, or multiple? _____ simple
- If a fleshy, simple fruit, what kind is it? (berry, drupe, or pome) _____ drupe
- If a dry, simple fruit, what kind is it? (legume, samara, nut, or achene) _____
- Describe it. _____ Brilliant red drupes in axillary clusters. Male trees do not produce berries.

Identifying the Tree

Using the observations you have made, find the tree in the *Peterson Guide*.
- Common name for this type of tree: _____ American Holly

Researching the Tree

Using the *Peterson Guide* and *The Tree Book*, we can learn more about this type of tree.
- What is the Latin name for this type of tree? _____ Ilex opaca
- From what Latin words is this name derived? _____ **Ilex, Ilicis** f.   *holm oak*
  opacu, -a, -um   *shady, dark*
- What is this type of tree's natural habitat? _____ It grows naturally in rich, moist woods, but is often planted as a decorative plant.
- What is the average height of this type of tree? _____ 40-50 ft.
- What type of wood does this tree have, and for what is it used? _____
  The wood is ivory in color and accepts dye evenly. It once was used for the white and black inlaid lines of furniture and musical instruments.

- Share any interesting facts or stories associated with this type of tree. _____
  The leaves and berries of the holly tree are often used as decoration during the Christmas season. They are specifically used for making wreaths.

Sketching

- Common name of the tree: _____
- In the space below, use the leaf sample you collected from the tree you observed, and, to the best of your ability, sketch a picture of the leaf.

Leaf

- In the space below, use the flower or fruit samples you collected, and, to the best of your ability, sketch a picture of each. If you were unable to collect a sample, use a picture in either the *Peterson Guide* or *The Tree Book*.

Flower	Fruit

Observing the Tree

Choose a tree to observe, and collect specimens of leaves, flowers, and fruit.

Structure and Location

- Where is the tree located? ___CHBC: at end of alley in library parking lot___
- What shape is its crown? (columnar, oval, round, vase-shaped, pyramidal, spreading, or weeping)___spreading___ Approximately how tall is it? _20-35 ft._

Bark

- What is the color and texture of the bark? (smooth, fissured, scaly, warty, or combination)
  The bark is gray and smooth with small fissures.

- Does the tree appear to be young or old? Why? _The bark is fissured; seems to be a mature tree._

Leaves

- Which of the two major categories of leaves does the tree possess? (broadleaf or needle-leaf)
  The leaf is a broadleaf.
- Does the tree appear to be deciduous or evergreen? _____deciduous_
- What is the texture of the leaf? (smooth, rough, fuzzy, hairy, or waxy) _____
  It is smooth and papery.
- What is its shape? (linear, oblong, ovate, lanceolate, elliptical, cordate, deltoid, or spatulate)
  The leaflets are elliptical.
- What is the leaf arrangement? (alternate, opposite, or whorled) _____alternate_____
- What is the leaf's venation? (pinnate or palmate) _____pinnate_____
- What is the nature of the leaf margin? (entire, toothed, lobed, or some combination)
  The leaflets are entire except for two small teeth at each base.
- Are the leaves single or compound? _____pinnately compound____
- Is there anything special about this leaf? _The leaves can have over 20 leaflets and reach over two
  feet long._

Flowers (If there are no flowers present, fill in this section after referencing the *Peterson Guide* or *The Tree Book*.)

- Does the tree produce flowers or cones?_____flowers____
- What size are the blooms? (large or small)_____small flowers but in large clusters_
- What color are the petals?_____yellowish green and red_

82

- Is the flower fragrant? _____ females don't stink; males give off strong unpleasant smell _____
- What type of flower is it? (staminate, pistillate, or perfect) _____ has both staminate and pistillate _____
- Is there anything special about this tree's flowers? _____ Male flowers give off a foul smell and are _____ the reason why the tree is sometimes called the "stink-weed." The female flowers are actually perfect (have stamen), but the stamen don't function. Male and female flowers are on separate trees.

Fruits (If there is no fruit present, fill in this section after referencing the *Peterson Guide* or *The Tree Book*.)
- Is the fruit fleshy or dry? _____ dry _____
- Is the fruit simple, aggregate, or multiple? _____ simple _____
- If a fleshy, simple fruit, what kind is it? (berry, drupe, or pome) _____
- If a dry, simple fruit, what kind is it? (legume, samara, nut, or achene) _____ samara _____
- Describe it. _____ The bright red and green samaras look almost like flower petals. The samaras are _____ found in large clusters called panicles.

Identifying the Tree

Using the observations you have made, find the tree in the *Peterson Guide*.
- Common name for this type of tree: _____ Tree of Heaven _____

Researching the Tree

Using the *Peterson Guide* and *The Tree Book*, we can learn more about this type of tree.
- What is the Latin name for this type of tree? _____ Ailanthus altissima _____
- From what Latin words is this name derived? _____ **ailanthus, -i** f. *tree of heaven or stink-weed* _____
  _____ **altissimus, -a, -um** *highest* _____
- What is this type of tree's natural habitat? _____ It is native to China, but introduced to the U.S. by _____ Europe. It can survive anywhere.
- What is the average height of this type of tree? _____ 40-50 ft. _____
- What type of wood does this tree have, and for what is it used? _____
  The Chinese use the wood to make steamers for food. However, due to its rapid and uneaven growth, the wood is not very useful for building. Its abundant supply makes it a good firewood.

- Share any interesting facts or stories associated with this type of tree. _____
  The Tree of Heaven was introduced to the U.S. for the silk industry. However, when the tree arrived, the silkworms did not survive, while the tree flourished. The name for the ailanthus in Chinese is "chouchun," which means "foul-smelling tree."

Sketching

- Common name of the tree: _____
- In the space below, use the leaf sample you collected from the tree you observed, and, to the best of your ability, sketch a picture of the leaf.

Leaf

- In the space below, use the flower or fruit samples you collected, and, to the best of your ability, sketch a picture of each. If you were unable to collect a sample, use a picture in either the *Peterson Guide* or *The Tree Book*.

Flower	**Fruit**

Observing the Tree

The Tree Book has the saucer magnolia, which is not quite the same as the specimen in the School of Music yard, a southern magnolia. Here is the information for the southern magnolia.

Choose a tree to observe, and collect specimens of leaves, flowers, and fruit.

Structure and Location

- Where is the tree located? __CHBC: School of Music yard__
- What shape is its crown? (columnar, oval, round, vase-shaped, pyramidal, spreading, or weeping)___spreading___ Approximately how tall is it? __25-30 ft.__

Bark

- What is the color and texture of the bark? (smooth, fissured, scaly, warty, or combination)
  ___The bark is brownish gray and scaly.___

- Does the tree appear to be young or old? Why? __The bark is scaly and the tree is quite large;__ seems to be a mature tree.

Leaves

- Which of the two major categories of leaves does the tree possess? (broadleaf or needle-leaf)
  ___The leaf is a broadleaf.___
- Does the tree appear to be deciduous or evergreen? ___partially evergreen___
- What is the texture of the leaf? (smooth, rough, fuzzy, hairy, or waxy) _____
  ___It is thick and waxy. The underside is fuzzy.___
- What is its shape? (linear, oblong, ovate, lanceolate, elliptical, cordate, deltoid, or spatulate)
  ___The leaflets are oval.___
- What is the leaf arrangement? (alternate, opposite, or whorled) ___alternate___
- What is the leaf's venation? (pinnate or palmate) ___pinnate___
- What is the nature of the leaf margin? (entire, toothed, lobed, or some combination)
  ___The leaf is entire___
- Are the leaves single or compound? ___single___
- Is there anything special about this leaf? __The tree does lose some leaves during the winter, but__ maintains a majority. It is another of the few trees that are both broadleaf and evergreen.

Flowers (If there are no flowers present, fill in this section after referencing the *Peterson Guide* or *The Tree Book*.)

- Does the tree produce flowers or cones? ___flowers___
- What size are the blooms? (large or small) ___very large cupped flowers___
- What color are the petals? ___white___

85

- Is the flower fragrant? _____ very fragrant _____
- What type of flower is it? (staminate, pistillate, or perfect) _____ perfect _____
- Is there anything special about this tree's flowers? _____ The flower has many pistils and stamens that grow into a cone-shaped fruit. _____

Fruits (If there is no fruit present, fill in this section after referencing the *Peterson Guide* or *The Tree Book*.)

- Is the fruit fleshy or dry? _____ dry _____
- Is the fruit simple, aggregate, or multiple? _____ aggregate _____
- If a fleshy, simple fruit, what kind is it? (berry, drupe, or pome) _____
- If a dry, simple fruit, what kind is it? (legume, samara, nut, or achene) _____
- Describe it. _____ Although it is aggregate, the fruit is a woody cone-like structure that has many sections called carpels. Each carpel contains 1 or 2 bright red seeds. _____

Identifying the Tree

Using the observations you have made, find the tree in the *Peterson Guide*.

- Common name for this type of tree: _____ Southern Magnolia _____

Researching the Tree

Using the *Peterson Guide* and *The Tree Book*, we can learn more about this type of tree.

- What is the Latin name for this type of tree? _____ Magnolia grandiflora _____
- From what Latin words is this name derived? _____

gandis, -e	*large, great*
flos, floris m.	*flower*

- What is this type of tree's natural habitat? _____ Normally found in southern U.S. _____

- What is the average height of this type of tree? _____ 20-30 ft. _____
- What type of wood does this tree have, and for what is it used? _____
  Hard, non-warping wood, used for slats for wood blinds.

- Share any interesting facts or stories associated with this type of tree. _____
  The southern magnolia is usually planted as an ornamental plant and normally has a pyramidal crown.

Sketching

- Common name of the tree: _____
- In the space below, use the leaf sample you collected from the tree you observed, and, to the best of your ability, sketch a picture of the leaf.

Leaf

- In the space below, use the flower or fruit samples you collected, and, to the best of your ability, sketch a picture of each. If you were unable to collect a sample, use a picture in either the *Peterson Guide* or *The Tree Book*.

Flower	**Fruit**

Observing the Tree

Choose a tree to observe, and collect specimens of leaves, flowers, and fruit.

Structure and Location

- Where is the tree located? __CHBC: west side of library by Frankfort__

- What shape is its crown? (columnar, oval, round, vase-shaped, pyramidal, spreading, or weeping)_____round/pyramidal_____ Approximately how tall is it? ___65-80 ft.___

Bark

- What is the color and texture of the bark? (smooth, fissured, scaly, warty, or combination)
  __The bark is dark brown to ashy gray and is deeply fissured in a zigzag or diamond pattern.__

- Does the tree appear to be young or old? Why? __The tree is tall and the bark is deeply fissured.__ __This seems to be a mature tree.__

Leaves

- Which of the two major categories of leaves does the tree possess? (broadleaf or needle-leaf)
  __The leaf is a broadleaf.__

- Does the tree appear to be deciduous or evergreen? _____deciduous_____

- What is the texture of the leaf? (smooth, rough, fuzzy, hairy, or waxy) _____
  __It is smooth and papery.__

- What is its shape? (linear, oblong, ovate, lanceolate, elliptical, cordate, deltoid, or spatulate)
  __The leaflets are ovate.__

- What is the leaf arrangement? (alternate, opposite, or whorled) _____opposite_____

- What is the leaf's venation? (pinnate or palmate) _____pinnate_____

- What is the nature of the leaf margin? (entire, toothed, lobed, or some combination)
  __The leaf has finely toothed margins.__

- Are the leaves single or compound? _____pinnately compound_____

- Is there anything special about this leaf? __The difference between a green ash and a white ash is__ __the pale color on the underside of the white ash leaf. It is a compound leaf that usually has 7 leaflets.__

Flowers (If there are no flowers present, fill in this section after referencing the *Peterson Guide* or *The Tree Book*.)

- Does the tree produce flowers or cones?_____flowers_____

- What size are the blooms? (large or small)_____Male and female flowers are small._____

- What color are the petals?_____Both male and female flowers are green and purple.

- Is the flower fragrant? _____ not noticeably _____
- What type of flower is it? (staminate, pistillate, or perfect) _____ has both staminate and pistillate
- Is there anything special about this tree's flowers? _____ Male and female flowers grow on separate trees. The female flowers occur in small inconspicuous clusters. _____

Fruits (If there is no fruit present, fill in this section after referencing the *Peterson Guide* or *The Tree Book*.)

- Is the fruit fleshy or dry? _____ dry _____
- Is the fruit simple, aggregate, or multiple? _____ simple _____
- If a fleshy, simple fruit, what kind is it? (berry, drupe, or pome) _____
- If a dry, simple fruit, what kind is it? (legume, samara, nut, or achene) _____ samara _____
- Describe it. _____ The samaras grow in clusters on female trees. _____

Identifying the Tree

Using the observations you have made, find the tree in the *Peterson Guide*.

- Common name for this type of tree: _____ White Ash _____

Researching the Tree

Using the *Peterson Guide* and *The Tree Book*, we can learn more about this type of tree.

- What is the Latin name for this type of tree? _____ Fraxinus Americana _____
- From what Latin words is this name derived? _____ **fraxinus, i** f. _____ *ash tree*

  Americanus, -a, -um _____ *American*
- What is this type of tree's natural habitat? _____ Found in open areas all over the eastern U.S. _____

- What is the average height of this type of tree? _____ 60-100 ft. _____
- What type of wood does this tree have, and for what is it used? _____

  The wood is light and hard and is readily used for sports equipment and tools, including baseball bats, oars, axe handles, and furniture. _____

- Share any interesting facts or stories associated with this type of tree. _____

  Ash is still the most commonly used wood baseball bat in the major leagues. _____

Sketching

- Common name of the tree: _____
- In the space below, use the leaf sample you collected from the tree you observed, and, to the best of your ability, sketch a picture of the leaf.

Leaf

- In the space below, use the flower or fruit samples you collected, and, to the best of your ability, sketch a picture of each. If you were unable to collect a sample, use a picture in either the *Peterson Guide* or *The Tree Book*.

Flower	**Fruit**

Lesson 16: Final Exam Review

Questions

1. What are the two systems found in plants? _____root and shoot_____

2. What are the two basic designs for plant roots? _____taproot and fibrous_____

3. _____xylem_____ carry water absorbed in the roots to the rest of the plant.

4. _____phloem_____ carry food made in the leaves to the stem and the roots.

5. What is the sticky substance that flows through the phloem? _____sap_____

6. What are cells? _____Cells are small units of life that make up larger organisms._____

7. What are the two types of plant stems? _____herbaceous and woody_____

8. What are the four types of land plants? _____trees, shrubs, herbs, and vines_____

9. A plant life cycle that takes one year to complete: _____annual_____

10. A plant life cycle that takes two years to complete: _____biennial_____

11. A plant life cycle that takes more than two years to complete: _____perennial_____

12. What are the two major categories of leaves? _____broadleaf and needle-leaf_____

13. Trees that lose their leaves in the winter are called _____deciduous_____, and trees that keep their leaves in the winter are called _____evergreen_____.

14. A tree with needle-leaves is called a _____conifer_____.

15. The primary function of a leaf is to produce _____food_____ through the process called _____photosynthesis_____.

16. Into what can a leaf bud grow? _____a new leaf, branch, or flower_____

17. Mesophyll cells have little food-making factories called _____chloroplasts_____ that contain the enzyme _____chlorophyll_____, which performs the process of photosynthesis and gives leaves their green color.

18. What is photosynthesis? _____It is the process by which leaves make food by means of sunlight and water._____

19. What is the function of flowers? _____Flowers produce seeds in order for the plant to reproduce._____

20. The sweet-tasting watery liquid produced by some flowers: _____nectar_____

21. The process of producing organisms according to its kind: _____reproduction_____

22. The process in which pollen is transferred from an anther to a stigma: _____pollination_____

23. A flower that has both male and female parts is called _____perfect_____.

24. Instead of flowers, conifers produce seeds by means of ____cones____.

25. The uniting of a sperm cell with an egg cell is called ____fertilization____.

26. What is the botanical definition of a fruit? ____A fruit is a seed-bearing structure that results from the fully developed ovary of the flower of a plant.____

27. What is the culinary definition of a fruit? ____A "kitchen fruit" is a seed-bearing structure that is sweet in taste and fleshy in composition.____

Diagrams and Labeling

- Label the parts of a woody stem.

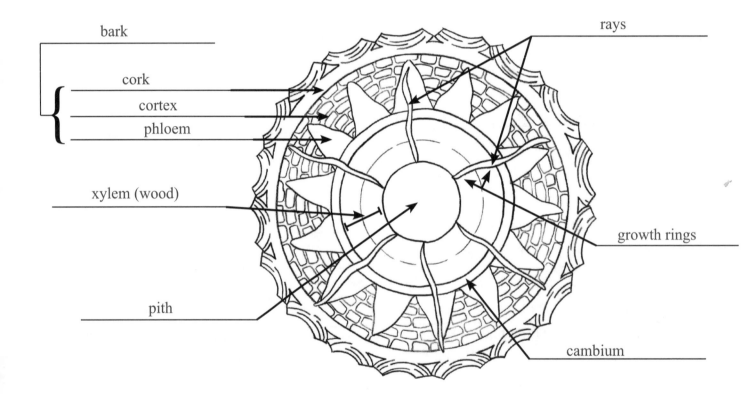

bark

cork

cortex

phloem

xylem (wood)

pith

rays

growth rings

cambium

- Label the different types of leaf arrangement.

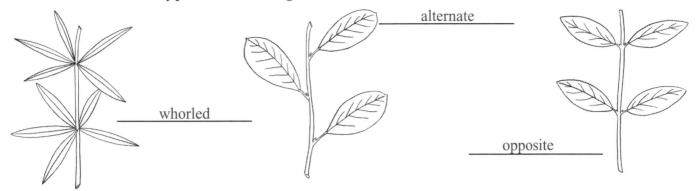

whorled

alternate

opposite

- Label the simple, compound, and twice compound leaves and their parts.

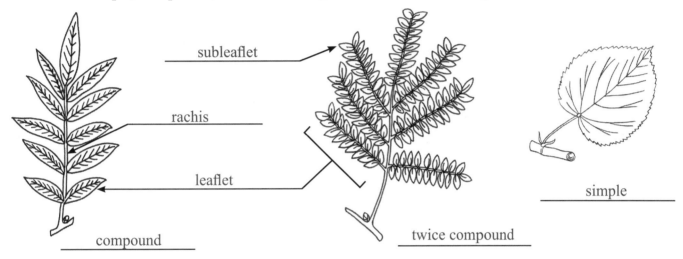

subleaflet

rachis

leaflet

compound

twice compound

simple

- Label the parts of a flower.

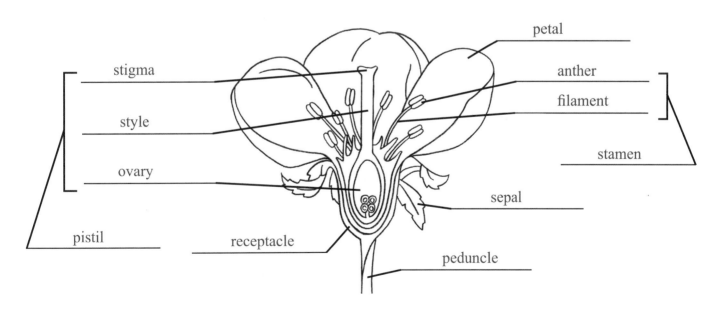

petal

anther

filament

stamen

stigma

style

ovary

pistil

receptacle

sepal

peduncle

Advanced Work

UNIT V
Photosynthesis & Respiration

Lesson 17: Photosynthesis I

Reading and Questions

The Book of Trees pp. 67-71 (2nd paragraph)

1. What does the term "photosynthesis" mean? ___It is a process of bringing things together by the means of light.___

2. The building blocks of life are called ___atoms___.

3. A group of atoms that all share the same characteristics is called an ___element___

4. What chart organizes all the known elements?___the Periodic Table___

5. What is a molecule? ___It is a combination of two or more atoms.___

6. In H_2O, how many atoms are present?___3___ How many elements? ___2___

7. In O_2, how many atoms are present?___2___ How many elements?___1___

8. In $C_6H_{12}O_6$, how many atoms are present?___24___ How many elements? ___3___

9. What does photosynthesis bring together? ___elements and molecules___

10. What molecules are being split up by the process of photosynthesis?___ ___water molecules and carbon dioxide molecules___

11. From where does the water come? ___the xylem___

12. What energy source is used to split up the molecules? ___sunlight___

13. What actually splits the molecules and rearranges them? ___chlorophyll___

14. Where is this enzyme located? ___the chloroplast___

15. Where are these little factories located? ___in the mesophyll___

16. What molecules result from photosynthesis? ___oxygen and glucose___

Diagrams and Labeling

- Label the elements involved in photosynthesis.

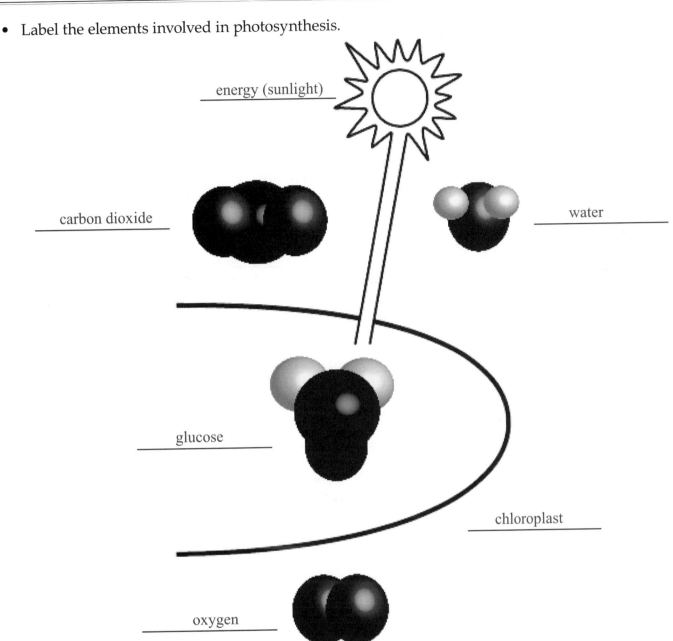

energy (sunlight)

carbon dioxide

water

glucose

chloroplast

oxygen

Activities

1. Survey the Periodic Table and find familiar elements. Find oxygen, hydrogen, and carbon. Why is the abbreviation for gold "Au" and the abbreviation for iron "Fe"?

   *Hint: *Second* and *Third Form Latin* students should know this!

2. On a classroom plant, house plant, or outside, take pieces of construction paper and cover parts of a few leaves and a whole leaf. Wait a week and compare the leaves that were covered with construction paper to the ones without. What happens when the leaf is unable to perform photosynthesis? Why wasn't the covered leaf able to do so?

Reading and Questions

The Book of Trees pp. 71 (3rd paragraph) -73

1. What takes the information in a chemical reaction and simplifies it into a formula resembling a mathematical equation? ___a chemical equation___

2. What are the molecules with which the chemical process starts called?___reactants___

3. What are the molecules called that result from the process?___products___

4. Glucose is a ___simple sugar___.

5. What phrase is helpful to remember the chemical equation for photosynthesis?
___"six, six, sugar, and six"___

6. For what is glucose used in plants and animals? ___It is used for energy and the production of___ ___proteins, fats, vitamins, cellulose, and other materials.___

7. Another name for table sugar is ___sucrose___.

8. Where can you find this substance? ___You can find sucrose in the phloem of trees.___

9. Write out the chemical equation for photosynthesis below, and label both products and reactants.

$$\overbrace{6\ CO_2 + 6\ H_2O}^{\text{reactants}} \rightarrow \overbrace{C_6H_{12}O_6 + 6\ O_2}^{\text{products}}$$

Chemical Equations

- Based on the reactants, determine the number of molecules for each product.

Teachers: The darkened number shows what was changed each step.

$$CH_4 + 2\ O_2 \rightarrow \underline{\ 1\ } CO_2 + \underline{\ 2\ } H_2O$$

Reactants:
C = 1
H = 4
O = 4

Products:
C = 1- 1
H = 2- **4**
O = 3- **4**

Teachers: Have the students write in what they currently have in the products. Then keep track of how that number changes when they change the coefficient (number of the molecule). Do that until the Products match the Reactants. These first two only require one change.

$$CH_4 + 4\ Cl_2 \rightarrow \underline{\ 1\ } CCl_4 + \underline{\ 4\ } HCl$$

Reactants:
C = 1
H = 4
Cl = 8

Products:
C = 1- 1
H = 1- **4**
Cl = 5- **8**

$$2\ C_8H_{16} + 24\ O_2\ \rightarrow\ \underline{\ 16\ }\ CO_2 + \underline{\ 16\ }\ H_2O$$

Reactants:
C = __16__
H = __32__
O = __48__

Products:
C = _1- **16**- 16_
H = _2- 2- **32**_
O = _3- **33**- 48_

*Teachers: This one requires two changes. 1st change carbon which results in the second set of numbers. 2nd change hydrogen (3rd set) and that balances the equation.

- Based on the products, determine the number of molecules for each reactant.

$$\underline{\ 4\ }\ Fe + \underline{\ 3\ }\ O_2\ \rightarrow\ 2\ Fe_2O_3$$

Reactants:
Fe = _1- **4**- 4_
O = _2- 2- **6**_

Products:
Fe = __4__
O = __6__

$$\underline{\ 1\ }\ C_3H_8 + \underline{\ 5\ }\ O_2\ \rightarrow\ 4\ H_2O + 3\ CO_2$$

Reactants:
C = _3- 3_
H = _8- 8_
O = _2- **10**_

Products:
C = __3__
H = __8__
O = __10__

$$\underline{\ 3\ }\ H_2O + \underline{\ 3\ }\ CO_2\ \rightarrow\ 3\ H_2CO_3$$

Reactants:
H = _2- **6**- 6_
C = _1- 1- **3**_
O = _3- **5**- 9_

Products:
H = __6__
C = __3__
O = __9__

Activities

1. **Challenge Exercise:** Balance these equations by determining BOTH the reactants and the molecules. Remember that increasing the coefficient (the number of molecules) multiplies each number of atoms in the molecule by that number. Start with the element of which there are fewest, and work through one element at a time.

$$\underline{\ 2\ }\ H_2 + \underline{\ 1\ }\ O_2\ \rightarrow\ \underline{\ 2\ }\ H_2O$$

Reactants:
H = _2- 2- **4**_
O = _2- 2- 2_

Products:
H = _2- **4**- 4_
O = _1- **2**- 2_

*Teachers: The only thing that is off is the O in the products, so you change it by making it 2 H_2O. This then throws the H off because you now have 4 H in the products and 2 in the reactants. You then just change the H in the reactants to 2 H_2. For the second equation, adjust in this order: H(2 steps)- O- Na

$$\underline{\ 2\ }\ Na + \underline{\ 2\ }\ H_2O\ \rightarrow\ \underline{\ 1\ }\ H_2 + \underline{\ 2\ }\ NaOH$$

Reactants:
H = _2- **4**- **4**- 4_
Na = _1- 1- 1- **2**_
O = _1- **2**- 2- 2_

Products:
H = _3- 3- **4**- 4_
Na = _1- 1- **2**- 2_
O = _1- 1- **2**- 2_

Lesson 19: Respiration I

Reading and Questions

The Book of Trees pp. 75-78 (1st paragraph)

1. What is cellular respiration? It is the process of releasing the energy in glucose for use in the cell.

2. What specific type of cellular respiration requires oxygen? aerobic respiration

3. What type of respiration uses yeast instead of oxygen and produces alcohol?
    fermentation

4. What is yeast? It is a single-celled organism that feeds on glucose.

5. What causes bread to rise? When yeast eats glucose, it produces alcohol and carbon dioxide. The carbon dioxide trapped in the dough causes it to fill with pockets of gas and rise.

6. What type of molecule is represented by the formula C_2H_5OH? alcohol (ethanol)

7. The energy that plants and animals get from respiration is called food energy

8. In what three forms does this type of energy come? sugars, starches, and cellulose

9. All forms of food energy that come from glucose are called carbohydrates

10. Write the formula that represents the ratio of atoms in this type of energy. CH_2O

11. What is a simple sugar? It is any single molecule that has the formula $C_6H_{12}O_6$.

12. What are the three types of simple sugars? glucose, fructose, and galactose

13. What is the only difference between these sugar molecules? The only difference is the arrangement of the molecules.

Chemical Equations

- Write out the chemical equation for aerobic respiration, and label the parts.

$$\underbrace{C_6H_{12}O_6 + 6\ O_2}_{\text{reactants}} \rightarrow \underbrace{6\ CO_2 + 6\ H_2O + \text{energy}}_{\text{products}}$$

- Write out the chemical equation for fermentation, and label the parts.

$$\underbrace{C_6H_{12}O_6 + \text{yeast}}_{\text{reactants}} \rightarrow \underbrace{2\ C_2H_5OH + 2\ CO_2 + \text{energy}}_{\text{products}}$$

Activities

1. Find either a healthy house plant or a thriving plant outside. Take plastic wrap and wrap it around one or a few of the leaves. As the leaf respirates, the water it produces won't be able to escape by evaporation, and condensation should form on the inside of the plastic wrap.

2. **Fermentation Experiment** (takes 15-30 minutes to complete)

   Materials you will need: plastic (or glass) bottles, warm water, sugar, dry active yeast, and uninflated balloons.

   Step 1: Fill bottle about halfway with warm water.

   Step 2: Dissolve sugar in the water. If there are multiple students, have them add different amounts and keep track of how much.

   Step 3: Have your balloon at the ready. Add the yeast and immediately cover the bottle opening with the balloon. Again, with multiple students, keep track of how much yeast was added. The yeast will eat the sugar (glucose) and produce CO_2. Since the gas cannot escape, it should fill up the balloon. After the experiment, assess what combination of sugar and yeast was most effective.

Lesson 20: Respiration II

Reading and Questions

The Book of Trees pp. 78 (2nd paragraph) -82

1. Simple sugars are referred to as ___monosaccharides___.

2. Table sugar is a combination of what two simple sugars? ___glucose and fructose___

3. Sucrose is an example of a ___disaccharide___.

4. What must happen before a cell can use the sugars in a disaccharide?___
   The disaccharide must be split up into its individual sugars.___

5. What is a starch, and why is it important to the life of a plant? ___
   A starch is a carbohydrate that is made from the combination of many simple sugars. It is important
   because it is the plant's way of storing energy for those times it doesn't have access to the sun.___

6. A starch is a ___polysaccharide___.

7. A starch consists of ___300-1,000___ glucose molecules that need to be broken down
   in order to be used, so it is a ___long-term___ source of energy.

8. A starch is also called a ___complex carbohydrate___.

9. What is an enzyme?___It is a special molecule that breaks starches apart into their individual
   simple sugars.___

10. Where are enzymes found in the human mouth?___in saliva___

11. ___Cellulose___ is a large polysaccharide found in plant cells that can have up to
    ___1,500___ linked glucose molecules.

12. Why can't humans break down cellulose? ___Humans lack the enzyme that breaks it down.___
    ___

13. Cellulose that can't be broken down by humans functions as ___fiber___
    in a human diet.

14. Why are vegetables important to a healthy diet? ___They contain vitamins and minerals that are
    essential to human development and health.___

Diagrams and Labeling

- Label these polysaccharides.

starch _____

cellulose _____

Activities

1. Take a bite of bread and hold it in your mouth without chewing. Notice that it grows slightly sweeter as you hold it in your mouth.

2. Take a potato, carrot, or an onion (or all three), and cut it up. Take half and place the pieces in a non-stick skillet. Set the other pieces aside. Cook the pieces in the skillet on medium heat until the carrot pieces and onion pieces carmelize*, or the potato pieces have become transparent. Then take your cooked pieces and raw pieces and compare them in taste. Why are the cooked pieces slightly sweeter?

   *Carmelization is a process that uses heat to break up disaccharides like sucrose, or polysaccharides like starch, into individual monosaccharides. During the process, the heat also browns the monosaccharides, which are characteristically transparent. Releasing the individual sugars in this way causes the vegetable or starch to sweeten in taste.

Lesson 21: Unit V Review

Questions

1. The process of bringing things together by means of light: _____photosynthesis_____

2. The building blocks of life are called _____atoms_____.

3. A group of atoms that all share the same characteristics is called an _____element_____

4. What chart organizes all the known elements? _____the Periodic Table_____

5. The combination of two or more atoms is called a _____molecule_____

6. What energy source is used to split up the molecules? _____sunlight_____

7. What actually splits the molecules and rearranges them? _____chlorophyll_____

8. Where is this enzyme located? _____the chloroplast_____

9. Where are these little factories located? _____in the mesophyll_____

10. A mathematical formula representing a chemical reaction: _____chemical equation_____

11. The starting molecules in a chemical equation are called the _____reactants_____, and the resulting molecules are called the _____products_____.

12. For what is glucose used in plants and animals? _____It is used for energy and the production of_____ proteins, fats, vitamins, cellulose, and other materials.

13. The process of releasing the energy in glucose for cell use: _____cellular respiration_____

14. What specific type of cellular respiration requires oxygen? _____aerobic respiration_____

15. Respiration that uses yeast instead of oxygen and produces alcohol: _____fermentation_____

16. What is yeast? _____It is a single-celled organism that feeds on glucose._____

17. The energy that plants and animals get from respiration is called _____food energy_____

18. All forms of food energy that come from glucose are called _____carbohydrates_____

19. What is a simple sugar? _____It is any single molecule that has the formula $C_6H_{12}O_6$._____

20. What are the three types of simple sugars? _____glucose, fructose, and galactose_____

21. What are the three types of carbohydrates? _____simple sugars, starch, and cellulose_____

22. Another name for a simple sugar: _____monosaccharide_____

23. A carbohydrate composed of two simple sugars: _____disaccharide_____

24. _____Starch_____ is a _____complex_____ carbohydrate composed of many glucose molecules and is used in plants for storage.

25. _____Cellulose_____ is a large carbohydrate that is found in plant cells.

26. A carbohydrate composed of many simple sugars: _____polysaccharide_____

27. A special molecule that can split another molecule or linked molecules: _____enzyme_____

Diagrams and Labeling

- Label the elements involved in photosynthesis.

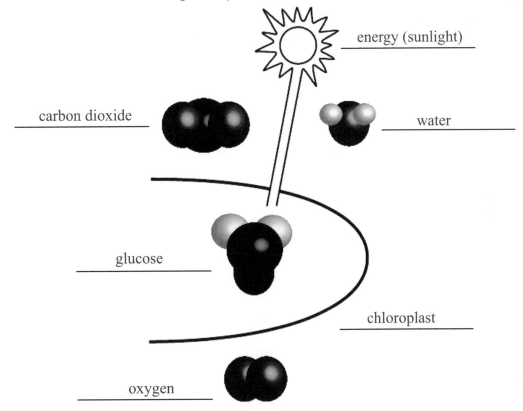

energy (sunlight)

carbon dioxide

water

glucose

chloroplast

oxygen

Chemical Equations

- Write out the chemical equation for photosynthesis, and label the parts.

reactants   products

$$6\ CO_2 + 6\ H_2O \rightarrow C_6H_{12}O_6 + 6\ O_2$$

- Write out the chemical equation for aerobic respiration, and label the parts.

reactants   products

$$C_6H_{12}O_6 + 6\ O_2 \rightarrow 6\ CO_2 + 6\ H_2O + energy$$

- Write out the chemical equation for fermentation, and label the parts.

reactants   products

$$C_6H_{12}O_6 + yeast \rightarrow 2\ C_2H_5OH + 2\ CO_2 + energy$$

- Based on the reactants, determine the number of molecules for each product.

$$C_3H_8 + 5\ O_2 \rightarrow \underline{\ 3\ }CO_2 + \underline{\ 4\ }H_2O$$

Reactants:
C = _3_
H = _8_
O = _10_

Products:
C = 1- **3**- 3
H = 2- 2- **8**
O = 3- **6**- **10**

$$2\ C_7H_6O_2 + 15\ O_2 \rightarrow \underline{\ 14\ }CO_2 + \underline{\ 6\ }H_2O$$

Reactants:
C = _14_
H = _12_
O = _34_

Products:
C = 1- **14**- 14
H = 2- 2- **12**
O = 3- **28**- **34**

- Based on the products, determine the number of molecules for each reactant.

$$\underline{\ 1\ }S_8 + \underline{\ 12\ }O_2 \rightarrow 8\ SO_3$$

Reactants:
S = 8- **8**
O = 2- **12**

Products:
S = _8_
O = _24_

$$\underline{\ 4\ }FeS_2 + \underline{\ 11\ }O_2 \rightarrow 2\ Fe_2O_3 + 8\ SO_2$$

Reactants:
Fe = 1- **4**- 4
S = 2- **8**- 8
O = 2- 2- **22**

Products:
Fe = _4_
S = _8_
O = _22_

- Balance these equations by determining BOTH the reactants and the molecules. *Hint: On the second one, start with balancing sulfur (S).

$$\underline{\ 3\ }O_2 \rightarrow \underline{\ 2\ }O_3$$

Reactants:
O = 2- 4- **6**

Products:
O = 3- 6- **6**

$$\underline{\ 8\ }H_2S + \underline{\ 8\ }Cl_2 \rightarrow \underline{\ 1\ }S_8 + \underline{\ 16\ }HCl$$

Reactants:
H= 2- **16**- 16- 16
S = 1- **8**- 8- 8
Cl = 2- 2- 2- **16**

Products:
H = 1- 1- **16**- 16
S = 8- 8- **8**- 8
Cl = 1- 1- **16**- 16

Quizzes, Tests, & Keys

Lesson 1 Quiz: *Plant Systems & Organs*

Name: _Io June Guidry_   Date: _9/2/16_   Score: _8⅔/10_

[86.66%

I. Label the plant systems and organs using the words from the word bank.

shoot system	root system	flower	leaf	stem

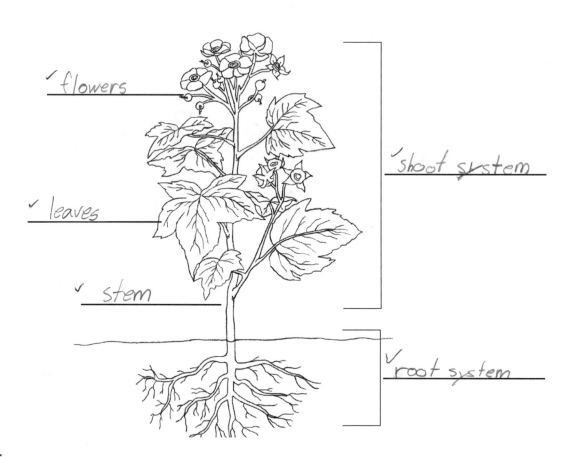

✓ flowers

✓ leaves

✓ stem

'shoot system

✓ root system

II. Short Answer

✓ 1. A structure of tissue that performs a particular function in an organism: _Organ_

✓ 2. A group of organs that work together to perform a particular function: _System_

✓ 3. What are the three organs that make up the shoot system? _stem, leaves, flowers_

⅓ ~ 4. What are the functions of the root system? _to anchor the plant..._
and absorb water ε nutrients, store food

⅓ ~ 5. What are the functions of the shoot system? _to help the plant to stay upright_
manufacture food ε reproduce by means of seeds

Lesson 2 Quiz: *The Root System*

Name: _____ Date: _____ Score: _____

I. Label the two different types of roots and the parts of a root.

cortex	epidermis	fibrous	phloem
root hair	taproot	vascular cylinder	xylem

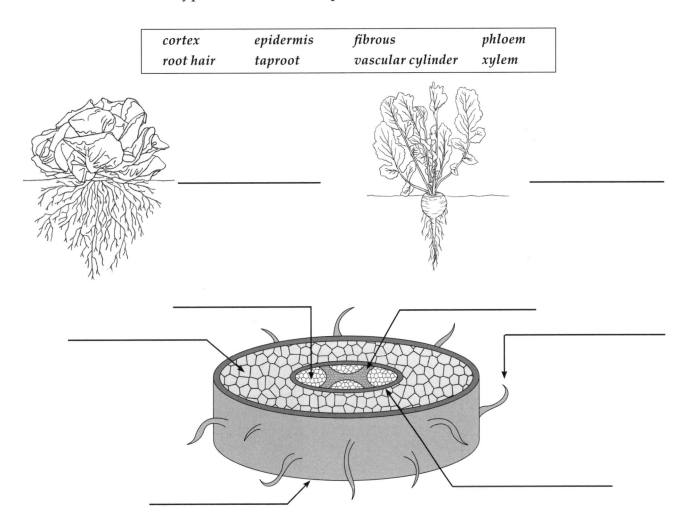

II. Short Answer

1. One primary root jutting straight into the ground:_____

2. A wide-spreading mass of roots without a primary root: _____

3. A carrot is an example of what specific type of taproot? _____

4. _____ help bring water and nutrients into the root.

5. The _____ stores food for later use.

6. In the vascular cylinder, the _____ carry water to the stem, and the

   _____ carry food to the root from the stem that was made in the leaves.

Lesson 3 Quiz: *External Structure of Stem*

Name: _____   Date: _____   Score: _____

I. Label the plants according to the four stem types.

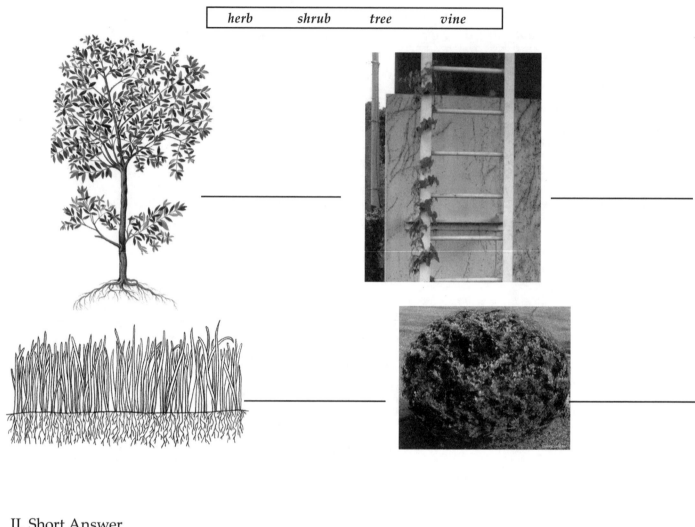

| herb | shrub | tree | vine |

_____

_____

_____

_____

II. Short Answer

1. What are the two types of plant stems? _____

2. A woody plant has cells that contain_____.

3. What is the life cycle of a plant?_____

   _____

4. A plant whose life cycle takes one year: _____

5. A plant whose life cycle takes two years: _____

6. A plant whose life cycle takes more than two years: _____

Lesson 4 Quiz: *Internal Structure of Stem*

Name: _____   Date: _____   Score: _____

I. Label the parts of a herbaceous and woody stem.

bark	cambium	cork	cortex	epidermis
growth rings	phloem	pith	rays	xylem

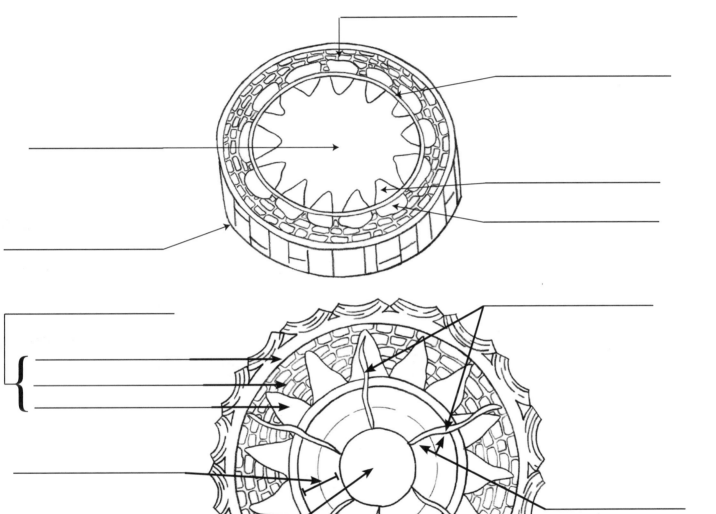

II. Short Answer

1. Spongy inner layer that stores water and disappears in woody stems: _____

2. Outermost layer of bark that protects a woody stem: _____

3. Slits in a woody stem that give the wood access to the food in the phloem:_____

Unit I Test

Name: _____   Date: _____   Score: _____

I. Describe each plant according to its stem type (there are two), stem structure (there are four), and root design (there are two). *Extra credit if you can specify between two similar types of roots.

1.

2.

3.

4.

5.

6.

1. _____

2. _____

3. _____

4. _____

5. _____

6. _____

II. Label the following diagrams for a plant root, herbaceous stem, and woody stem.

| bark | cambium | cork | cortex | growth rings | epidermis |
| phloem | pith | rays | root hair | vascular cylinder | xylem |

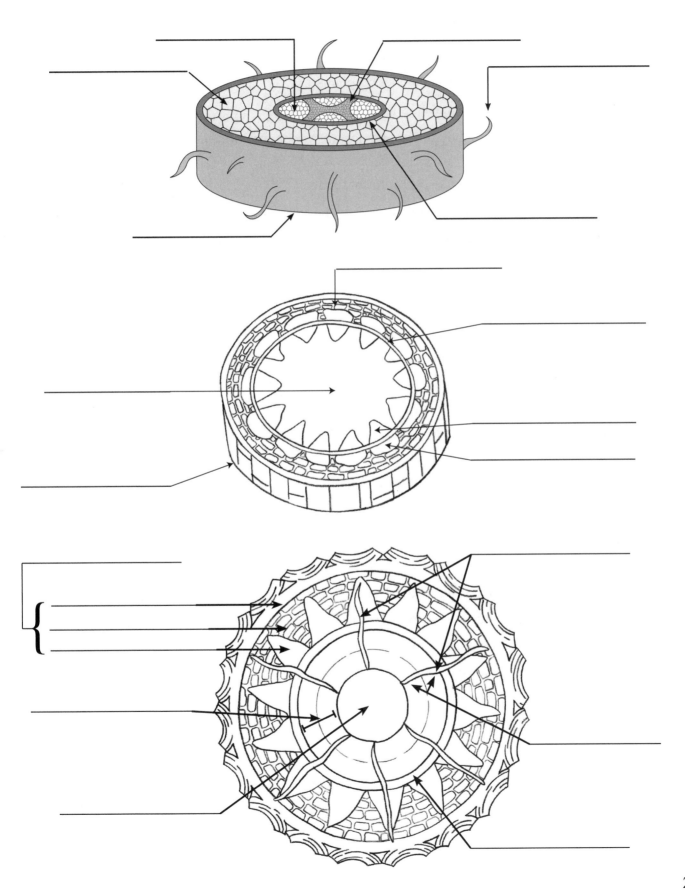

III. Matching

_____ 1. transports food made in the leaves down to the stem and roots

_____ 2. a structure of tissue that performs a particular function in an organism

_____ 3. a plant life cycle that takes two years to complete

_____ 4. a ring of cells that separates the phloem from the xylem and creates new layers of xylem in woody plants

_____ 5. small units of life that make up larger organisms

_____ 6. anchors the plant to the ground and absorbs water and nutrients from the ground

_____ 7. a plant life cycle that takes a year to complete

_____ 8. transports water absorbed by the roots to the rest of the plant

_____ 9. a group of organs that work together to perform a particular function for an organism

_____ 10. supports the leaves and reproductive parts of the plant, transports food and water, and acts as a storage facility for food

_____ 11. sticky substance that flows through phloem

_____ 12. thickened layer of cells that provides protection for the root and herbaceous stems

_____ 13. substance contained in the xylem of all woody plants

_____ 14. spongy layer that stores water, but eventually disappears in a woody stem

_____ 15. a layer of thinly walled cells that store food

_____ 16. a plant life cycle that takes more than two years to complete

A. annual
B. biennial
C. cambium
D. cortex
E. cells
F. epidermis
G. lignin
H. organ
I. perennial
J. phloem
K. pith
L. roots
M. sap
N. stem
O. system
P. xylem

IV. Short Answer

1. What are the two systems found in plants? _____

2. What are the organs that make up the shoot system? _____

3. What are the two types of plant stems? _____

4. What are the three areas of a woody stem? _____

V. Extra Credit

1. What is the difference between heartwood and sapwood? _____

_____

2. What are the different bark textures? _____

_____

3. A tree begins its life with what type of root system? _____

Lesson 6 Quiz: *External Structure of Leaf I*

Name: _____   Date: _____   Score: _____

I. Label the different leaf shapes.

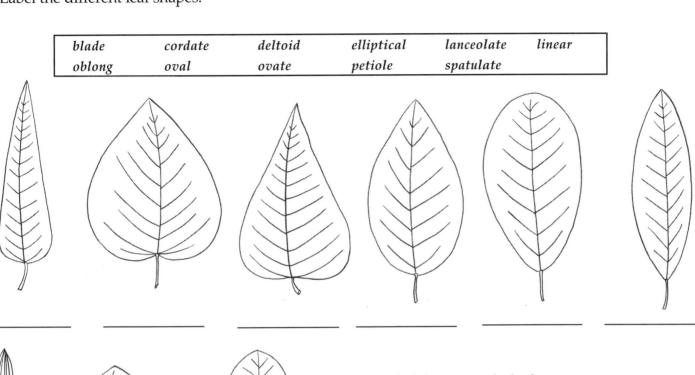

| blade | cordate | deltoid | elliptical | lanceolate | linear |
| oblong | oval | ovate | petiole | spatulate | |

_____ _____ _____ _____ _____ _____

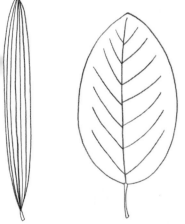

II. Label the parts of a leaf.

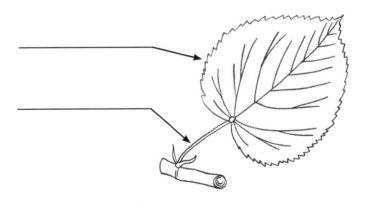

_____ _____ _____

III. Short Answer

1. What is the primary function of the leaf? _____

_____

2. What are the two major categories of leaves?_____

3. Trees that lose their leaves in the winter: _____

4. Trees that keep their leaves during the winter: _____

5. Trees with needle-leaves: _____

6. What are the different leaf textures? _____

_____

Lesson 7 Quiz: *External Structure of Leaf II*

Name: _____   Date: _____   Score: _____

alternate	*bud scar*	*entire*	*internode*	*lateral bud*	*leaflet*
lobed	*opposite*	*palmate*	*parallel*	*pinnate*	*rachis*
subleaflet	*terminal bud*	*toothed*	*whorled*		

I. Label the types of leaf arrangement.

II. Label the parts of a branch.

_____   _____   _____

III. Label the venation and margin.

venation:_____

margin:_____

venation:_____

margin:_____

IV. Label the parts of a compound leaf.

venation:_____

margin:_____

V. Short Answer

1. The place at which a leaf or leaves grow on a branch is called the _____

2. The angle at which the leaf grows from the branch is called the _____.

3. Into what can a leaf bud grow? _____

4. A leaf that is neither compound nor twice compound is called _____

Lesson 8 Quiz: *Internal Structure of Leaf*

Name: _____   Date: _____   Score: _____

cuticle	guard cells	lower epidermis	mesophyll	palisade layer
spongy layer	stoma	upper epidermis	vein	xylem & phloem

I. Label the internal parts of a leaf.

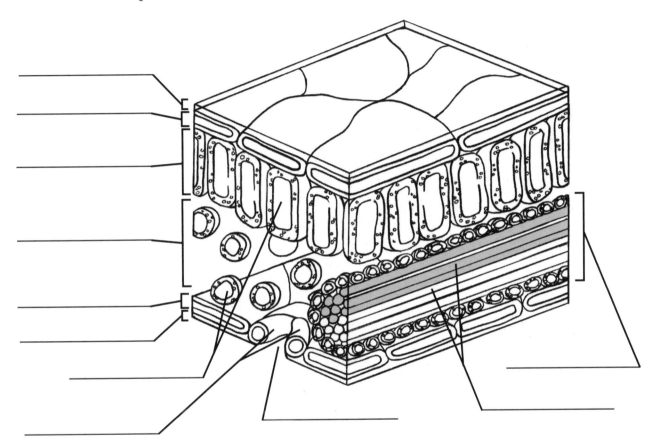

II. Short Answer

1. What is the primary function of leaves? _____

2. What is the function of stomata? _____

_____

3. What three elements are required for photosynthesis? _____

4. _____ open and close the stomata so that the leaf doesn't dry out.

5. The cells that give color to the leaf are called _____.

6. Mesophyll cells have little food-making factories called _____ that

contain the enzyme _____, which performs the process of

photosynthesis and gives leaves their green color.

Unit II Test

Name: _____   Date: _____   Score: _____

I. Match the leaf shapes.

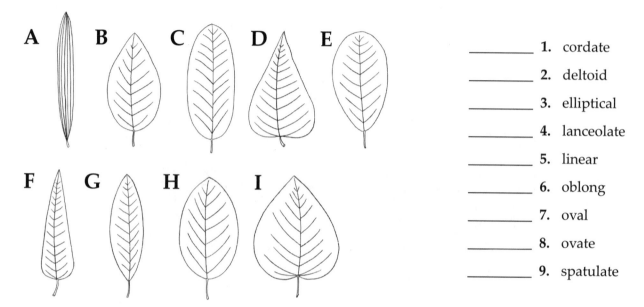

_____ **1.** cordate

_____ **2.** deltoid

_____ **3.** elliptical

_____ **4.** lanceolate

_____ **5.** linear

_____ **6.** oblong

_____ **7.** oval

_____ **8.** ovate

_____ **9.** spatulate

II. Label the venation, margin, and parts of a leaf.

| blade | entire | lobed | midrib | parallel |
| palmate | petiole | pinnate | toothed | |

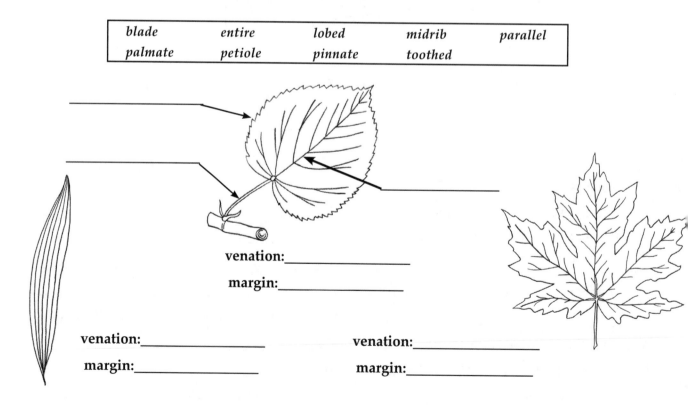

venation:_____

margin:_____

venation:_____

margin:_____

venation:_____

margin:_____

alternate	bud scar	cuticle	guard cells	internode	lateral bud
leaflet	lower epidermis	mesophyll	palisade layer	opposite	palmately compound
parallel	pinnately compound	rachis	spongy layer	stoma	twice compound
terminal bud	upper epidermis	vein	whorled	subleaflet	xylem & phloem

III. Label the following diagrams for leaf arrangement, parts of a branch, parts of compound leaf, and internal parts of a leaf.

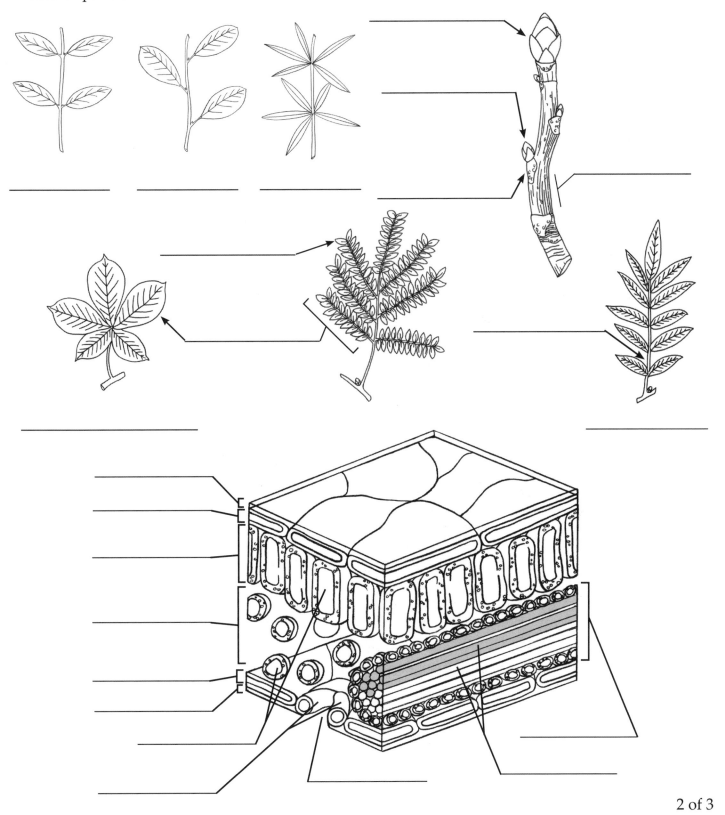

IV. Matching

_____ **1.** arrangement of veins in a leaf

_____ **2.** "like a palm"

_____ **3.** tiny openings in the bottom of a leaf that allow gases in and out

_____ **4.** a tree with needle-leaves

_____ **5.** transports food made in the leaves down to the stem and roots

_____ **6.** "like a feather"

_____ **7.** trees that shed their leaves in the winter

_____ **8.** enzyme in the mesophyll that gives the cell its green color

_____ **9.** a leaf with no petiole

_____ **10.** transports water absorbed by the roots to the rest of the plant

_____ **11.** angle at which a leaf grows from the branch

_____ **12.** a leaf with multiple blades for every petiole

_____ **13.** factory-like parts of the mesophyll in which photosynthesis takes place

_____ **14.** trees that keep their leaves during the winter

_____ **15.** vascular structures that contain the xylem and phloem

_____ **16.** a leaf with a single blade for every petiole

A. axil
B. chlorophyll
C. chloroplasts
D. compound
E. conifer
F. deciduous
G. evergreen
H. palmate
I. phloem
J. pinnate
K. sessile
L. simple
M. stomata
N. veins
O. venation
P. xylem

V. Short Answer

1. What are the two major categories of leaves?_____

2. What is the primary function of leaves? _____

_____

3. What three elements are needed for photosynthesis? _____

4. Into what can a leaf bud grow? _____

VI. Extra Credit

1. What is the difference between hardwood and softwood, and why is that distinction misleading?

_____

_____

_____

2. Why can't you see the other pigments present in the leaf? _____

_____

_____

Lesson 10 Quiz: *Structure of Flowers & Perfect Flower*

Name: _____   Date: _____   Score: _____

anther	female cone	filament	male cone	ovary	peduncle
perfect	petal	pistil	pistillate	receptacle	sepal
stamen	staminate	stigma	style		

I. Label the parts of a flower.

II. Label the types of flowers.

III. Label the types of cones.

IV. Short Answer

1. What is the function of flowers? _____

2. The process of producing organisms according to its kind: _____

3. A flower's collection of petals is called its _____.

4. The male part of the flower produces _____. The female: _____ .

5. A scientist that studies plants: _____

6. A flower that has both male and female parts is called _____, and a flower that only has one or the other is called _____.

7. Instead of flowers, _____ produce seeds by means of _____.

Lesson 11 Quiz: *Pollination & Fertilization*

Name: _____   Date: _____   Score: _____

anther	egg cell	filament	ovary	peduncle
petal	pollen	pollen tube	pollination	sepal
stamen	stigma	style		

I. Label the parts of a flower during fertilization.

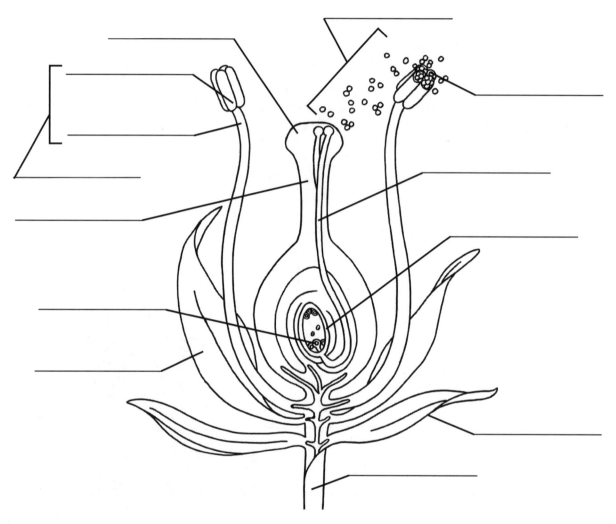

II. Short Answer

1. Male reproductive cells are called _____.
2. The process in which pollen is transferred from an anther to a stigma: _____
3. The sweet-tasting watery liquid produced by some flowers: _____
4. Pollination that occurs by the help of insects and animals:_____
5. Pollination that occurs by the help of wind and water: _____
6. The uniting of the sperm cells with the egg cells is called _____.
7. Fertilized egg cells will develop into _____.

Lesson 12 Quiz: *Simple Fleshy Fruits*

Name: _____   Date: _____   Score: _____

I. Label the following fruits according to whether they are berries, drupes, or pomes, and whether they are considered culinary fruits, culinary vegetables, or culinary nuts.

1. olive _____

2. watermelon _____

3. pear _____

4. grape _____

5. pumpkin _____

6. walnut _____

7. plum_____

8. jalapeño pepper _____

9. banana _____

II. Short Answer

1. Fruit develops from the _____ of the flower.
2. What is the function of a fruit? _____
   _____
3. Seed-bearing structure that develops from the ovary of a flower: _____
4. Seed-bearing structure that is sweet in taste and fleshy in composition: _____
5. What are the three categories of fruit? _____
6. A fruit that grows from a single flower with a single pistil: _____
7. What are the two types of simple fruit? _____
8. A simple fruit that is fleshy and juicy throughout: _____
9. A simple fruit that is fleshy with a stone in the center: _____
10. A simple fruit that is fleshy with a papery inside layer:_____
11. An apple is formed from the entire _____ of the flower.

Lesson 13 Quiz: *Simple Dry Fruits; Aggregate & Multiple Fruits; & Dispersal*

Name: _____ Date: _____ Score: _____

I. Label the following fruits according to whether they are legumes, samaras, nuts, achenes, grains, aggregate fruits, or multiple fruits.

1. raspberry _____

2. sunflower seed _____

3. pea _____

4. pineapple _____

5. maple tree seed _____

6. acorn _____

7. wheat _____

8. strawberry _____

9. rice _____

10. peanut _____

II. Short Answer

1. A simple dry fruit that consists of a pod enclosing several seeds: _____

2. These pods can be _____ or _____.

3. A seed with a papery wing that causes it to spin away from the tree: _____

4. A simple dry fruit in which the seed is enclosed by a thick shell: _____

5. A simple dry fruit with a thin shell that is mistaken for the nut: _____

6. A simple dry fruit that comes from grass and has a thin shell that is attached to the seed:

   _____

7. A cluster of individual fruit structures grown from the same flower: _____

8. A compound fruit that develops from a cluster of individual flowers: _____

Unit III Test

Name: _____ Date: _____ Score: _____

anther	egg cell	female cone	filament	male cone
ovary	peduncle	perfect	petal	pistil
pistillate	pollen	pollen tube	pollination	receptacle
sepal	stamen	staminate	stigma	style

I. Label the parts of a flower during fertilization, types of flowers, and types of cones.

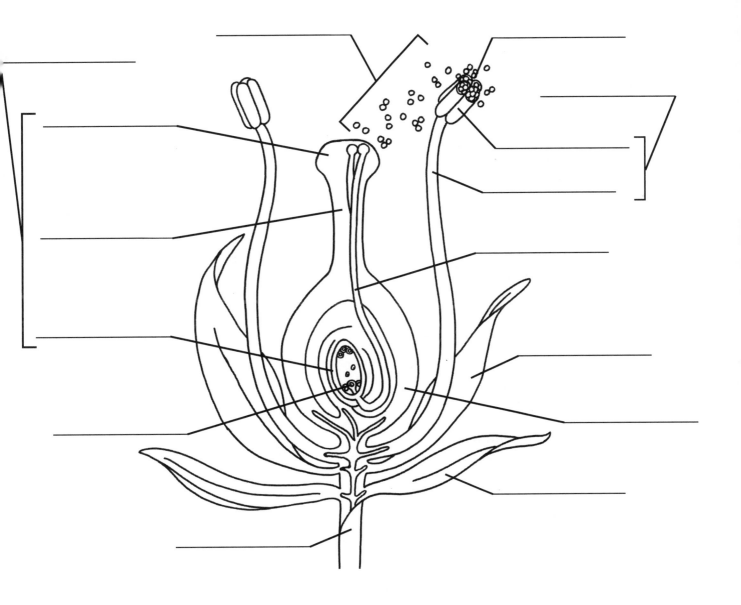

II. Label the following diagrams for types of flowers and types of cones.

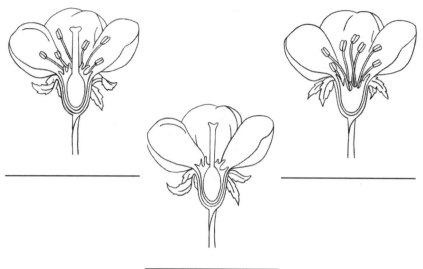 

_____   _____

_____

_____

III. Match the fruit to the correct description.

_____ **1.** simple, dry achene

_____ **2.** simple, fleshy pome

_____ **3.** simple, dry grain

_____ **4.** simple, dry nut

_____ **5.** simple, fleshy berry

_____ **6.** simple, dry legume

_____ **7.** fleshy, multiple fruit

_____ **8.** fleshy, aggregate fruit

_____ **9.** simple, fleshy drupe

_____ **10.** simple, dry samara

A.   acorn
B.   apple
C.   cherry
D.   maple tree seed
E.   pea
F.   pineapple
G.   strawberry
H.   sunflower seed
I.   watermelon
J.   wheat

IV. Short Answer

1. What is the function of flowers? _____

    _____

2. The ovary produces _____, and the anther produces_____

3. What is pollination?_____

4. What is the botanical definition of a fruit? _____

    _____

5. What is the culinary definition of a fruit? _____

    _____

V. Matching

_____ 1. simple fruit that is fleshy and juicy throughout

_____ 2. the uniting of a sperm cell with an egg cell

_____ 3. pollination that occurs without the help of a living thing

_____ 4. leaf-like appendages that protect the flower bud

_____ 5. stalk that attaches the flower to the stem

_____ 6. simple dry fruit with a thin shell that is mistaken for the nut

_____ 7. seed with a papery wing that causes it to spin away from the tree

_____ 8. compound fruit that develops from a cluster of individual flowers

_____ 9. producing organisms according to its kind

_____ 10. sweet-tasting, watery liquid produced by some flowers

_____ 11. cluster of individual fruit structures grown from the same flower

_____ 12. flower that only has the male part

_____ 13. simple dry fruit that consists of a woody or herbaceous pod enclosing several seeds

_____ 14. a flower's collection of petals

_____ 15. flower that only has the female part

_____ 16. simple fruit that is fleshy with a woody stone in the center

_____ 17. simple dry fruit in which the seed is enclosed by a thick shell

_____ 18. a flower missing either stamen or a pistil

_____ 19. a flower with both stamen and a pistil

_____ 20. simple fruit that is fleshy with a papery inside layer

_____ 21. having to do with use in the kitchen

_____ 22. fruit that grows from a single flower with a single pistil

_____ 23. pollination that occurs by the help of a living thing

_____ 24. what conifers use to produce seeds instead of flowers

_____ 25. simple dry fruit that comes from grass and has a thin shell that is attached to the seed

A. abiotic
B. achene
C. aggregate fruit
D. berry
E. biotic
F. cones
G. corolla
H. culinary
I. drupe
J. fertilization
K. grain
L. incomplete
M. legume
N. multiple fruit
O. nectar
P. nut
Q. peduncle
R. perfect
S. pistillate
T. pome
U. reproduction
V. samara
W. sepals
X. simple fruit
Y. staminate

VI. Extra Credit

1. Why are flowers' petals so colorful? _____

_____

2. Why is the nectar located at the bottom of the flower? _____

_____

_____

_____

3. An apple is formed from the entire _____ of the flower.

Trees Final

Name: _____ Date: _____ Score: _____

alternate	*anther*	*cambium*	*peduncle*	*xylem*	*twice (bi) compound*
cortex	*pith*	*filament*	*growth rings*	*leaflet*	*opposite*
ovary	*style*	*palmately compound*	*petal*	*phloem*	*pinnately compound*
pistil	*rays*	*rachis*	*receptacle*	*sepal*	*stamen*
stigma	*bark*	*subleaflet*	*whorled*	*cork*	

I. Label the following diagrams for parts of a woody stem, parts of a flower, leaf arrangements, parts of a compound leaf, and the elements involved in photosynthesis.

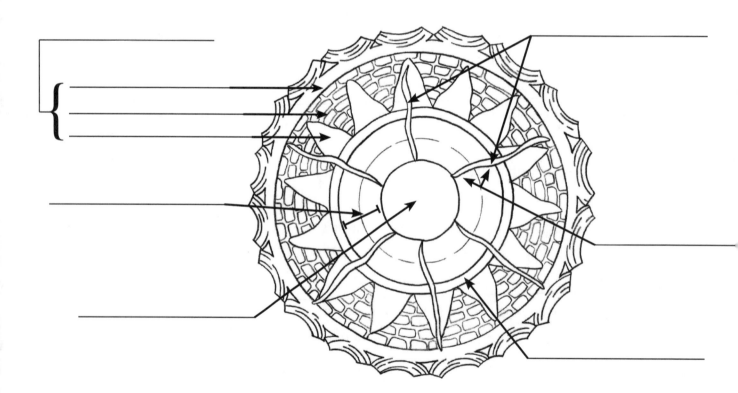

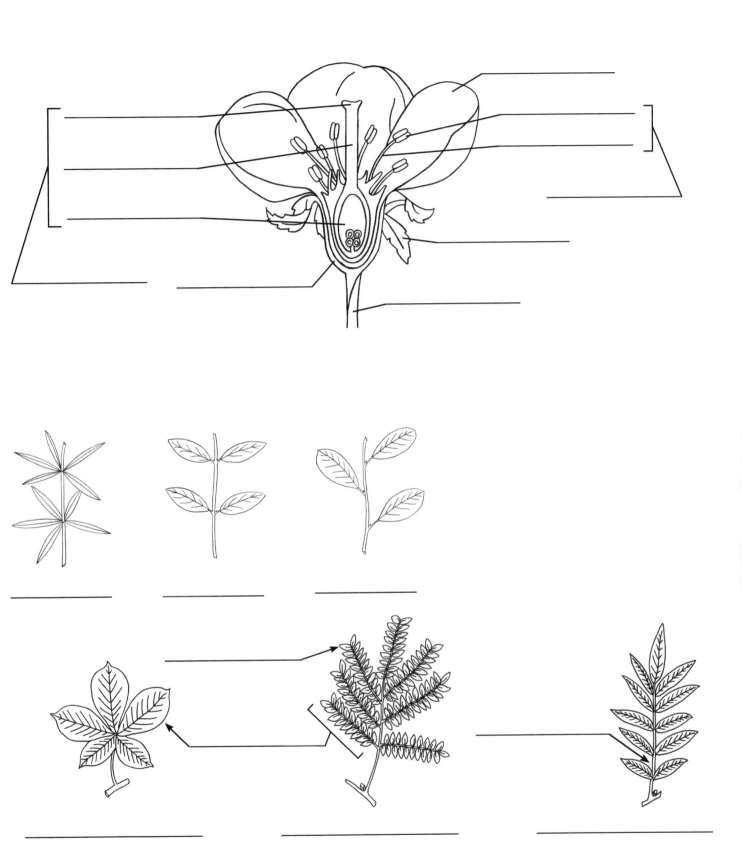

II. Short Answer

1. What are the two systems found in plants? _____

2. What are the two types of plant stems? _____

3. What are the two major categories of leaves?_____

4. What is the primary function of leaves? _____

   _____

5. Into what can a leaf bud grow? _____

6. What is photosynthesis? _____

   _____

7. What is the function of flowers? _____

   _____

8. What is the botanical definition of a fruit? _____

   _____

9. What is the culinary definition of a fruit? _____

   _____

III. Matching

_____ 1. a tree with needle-leaves

_____ 2. trees that shed their leaves in the winter

_____ 3. food-making factories in the mesophyll

_____ 4. trees that keep their leaves during the winter

_____ 5. transports food made in the leaves down to the stem and roots

_____ 6. a plant life cycle that takes two years to complete

_____ 7. small units of life that make up larger organisms

_____ 8. anchors the plant to the ground and absorbs water and nutrients from the ground

_____ 9. a plant life cycle that takes a year to complete

_____ 10. transports water absorbed by the roots to the rest of the plant

_____ 11. process in which pollen is transferred from an anther to a stigma

_____ 12. a plant life cycle that takes more than two years to complete

_____ 13. enzyme in the mesophyll that makes photosynthesis possible and gives green leaves their color

_____ 14. the uniting of a sperm cell with an egg cell

_____ 15. producing organisms according to its kind

_____ 16. sweet-tasting, watery liquid produced by some flowers

_____ 17. flower that only has the male part

_____ 18. flower that only has the female part

_____ 19. a flower with both stamen and a pistil

_____ 20. what conifers use to produce seeds instead of flowers

A. annual
B. biennial
C. cells
D. chlorophyll
E. chloroplasts
F. cones
G. conifer
H. deciduous
I. evergreen
J. fertilization
K. nectar
L. perennial
M. perfect
N. pistillate
O. pollination
P. phloem
Q. reproduction
R. roots
S. staminate
T. xylem

IV. Extra Credit

1. What is the difference between a tree and a shrub? _____

_____

2. How do you classify a tomato? _____

_____

_____

Lesson 1 Quiz: *Plant Systems & Organs*

Name: _____**KEY**_____ Date: _____ Score: _____

I. Label the plant systems and organs using the words from the word bank.

shoot system	*root system*	*flower*	*leaf*	*stem*

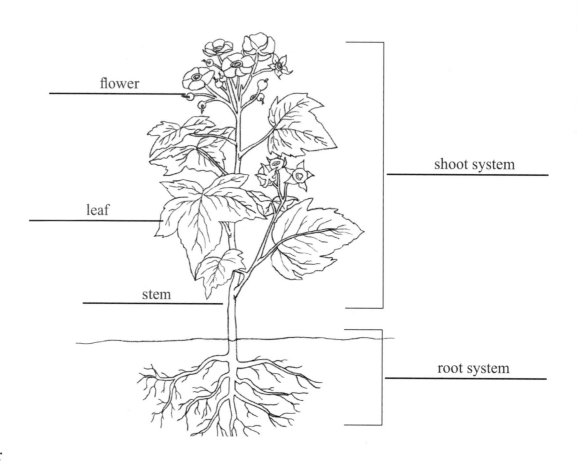

flower

leaf

stem

shoot system

root system

II. Short Answer

1. A structure of tissue that performs a particular function in an organism: _____ organ _____

2. A group of organs that work together to perform a particular function: _____ system _____

3. What are the three organs that make up the shoot system? _____ stem, leaf, and flower _____

4. What are the functions of the root system? _____ The root system anchors the plant and performs _____ the functions of absorbing water and nutrients and storing food.

5. What are the functions of the shoot system? _____ The shoot system holds the plant upright, _____ manufactures food, and reproduces the plant by means of seeds.

Lesson 2 Quiz: *The Root System*

Name: _____**KEY**_____ Date: _____ Score: _____

I. Label the two different types of roots and the parts of a root.

cortex	*epidermis*	*fibrous*	*phloem*
root hair	*taproot*	*vascular cylinder*	*xylem*

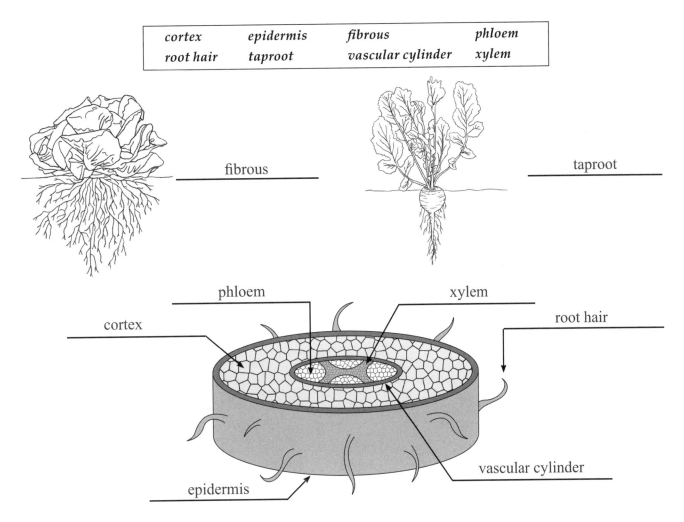

fibrous _____

taproot _____

phloem

xylem

cortex

root hair

epidermis

vascular cylinder

II. Short Answer

1. One primary root jutting straight into the ground:_____taproot_____

2. A wide-spreading mass of roots without a primary root: _____fibrous root_____

3. A carrot is an example of what specific type of taproot? _____food-storing taproot_____

4. _____Root hairs_____ help bring water and nutrients into the root.

5. The _____cortex_____ stores food for later use.

6. In the vascular cylinder, the _____xylem_____ carry water to the stem, and the
_____phloem_____ carry food to the root from the stem that was made in the leaves.

Lesson 3 Quiz: *External Structure of Stem*

Name: _____**KEY**_____   Date: _____   Score: _____

I. Label the plants according to the four stem types.

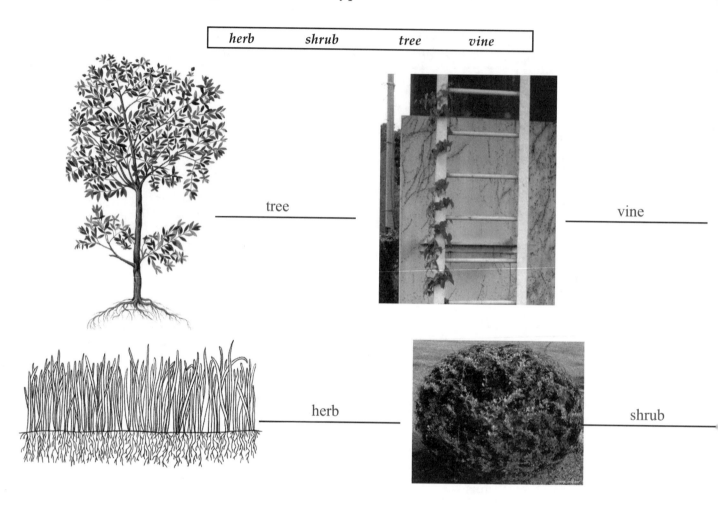

| *herb* | *shrub* | *tree* | *vine* |

tree

vine

herb

shrub

II. Short Answer

1. What are the two types of plant stems? _____herbaceous and woody_____

2. A woody plant has cells that contain_____lignin_____.

3. What is the life cycle of a plant?_____A plant life cycle consists of germinating, flowering, producing seeds, and dying._____

4. A plant whose life cycle takes one year: _____annual_____

5. A plant whose life cycle takes two years: _____biennial_____

6. A plant whose life cycle takes more than two years: _____perennial_____

Lesson 4 Quiz: *Internal Structure of Stem*

Name: _____**KEY**_____   Date: _____   Score: _____

I. Label the parts of a herbaceous and woody stem.

bark	cambium	cork	cortex	epidermis
growth rings	phloem	pith	rays	xylem

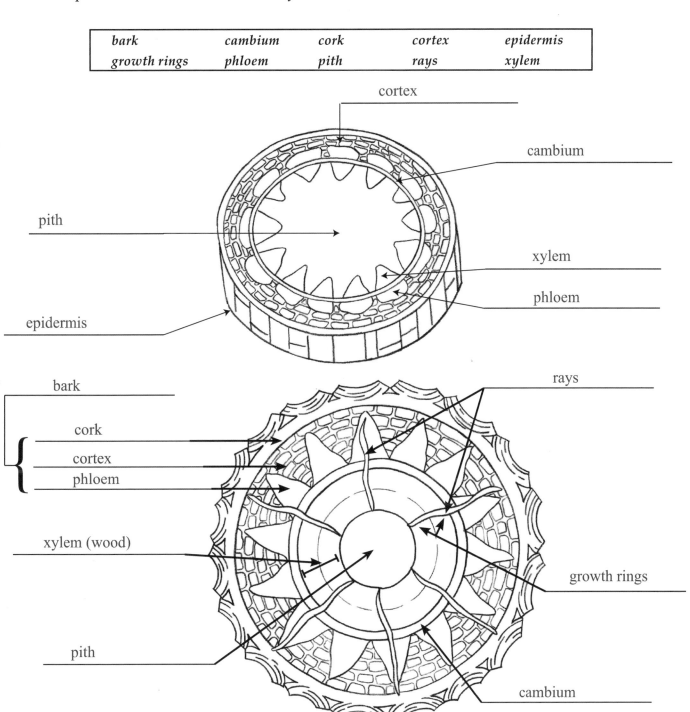

II. Short Answer

1. Spongy inner layer that stores water and disappears in woody stems: _____pith_____
2. Outermost layer of bark that protects a woody stem: _____cork_____
3. Slits in a woody stem that give the wood access to the food in the phloem:_____rays_____

Unit I Test

Name: **KEY**   Date: _____   Score: _____

I. Describe each plant according to its stem type (there are two), stem structure (there are four), and root design (there are two). *Extra credit if you can specify between two similar types of roots.

1.

2.

3.

4.

5.

6.

1. ___herbaceous stem, herb, taproot *non-storage taproot___
2. ___woody stem, tree, fibrous root___
3. ___herbaceous stem, herb, taproot *food-storing taproot___
4. ___herbaceous stem, herb, fibrous___
5. ___woody stem, shrub, fibrous root___
6. ___herbaceous stem, vine, fibrous *it's hard to tell from picture, so accept herbaceous or woody stem___

II. Label the following diagrams for a plant root, herbaceous stem, and woody stem.

bark	cambium	cork	cortex	growth rings	epidermis
phloem	pith	rays	root hair	vascular cylinder	xylem

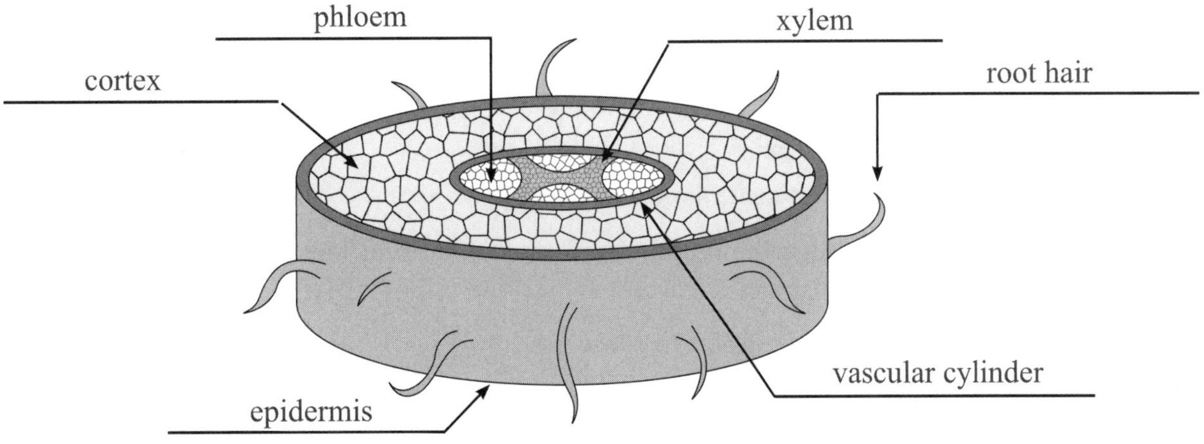

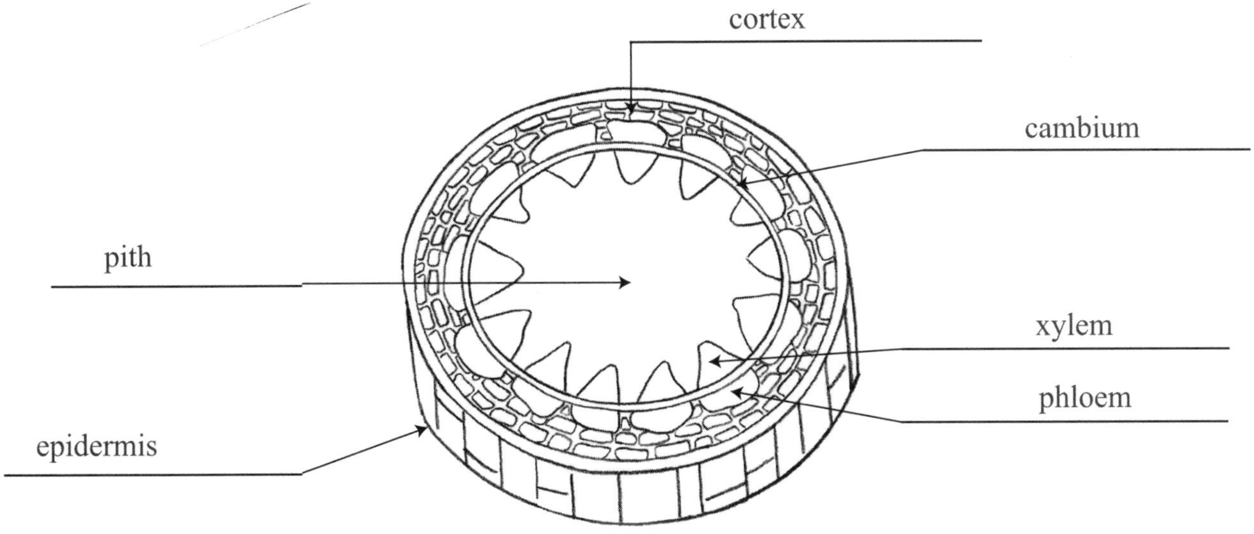

phloem

xylem

cortex

root hair

epidermis

vascular cylinder

cortex

cambium

pith

xylem

phloem

epidermis

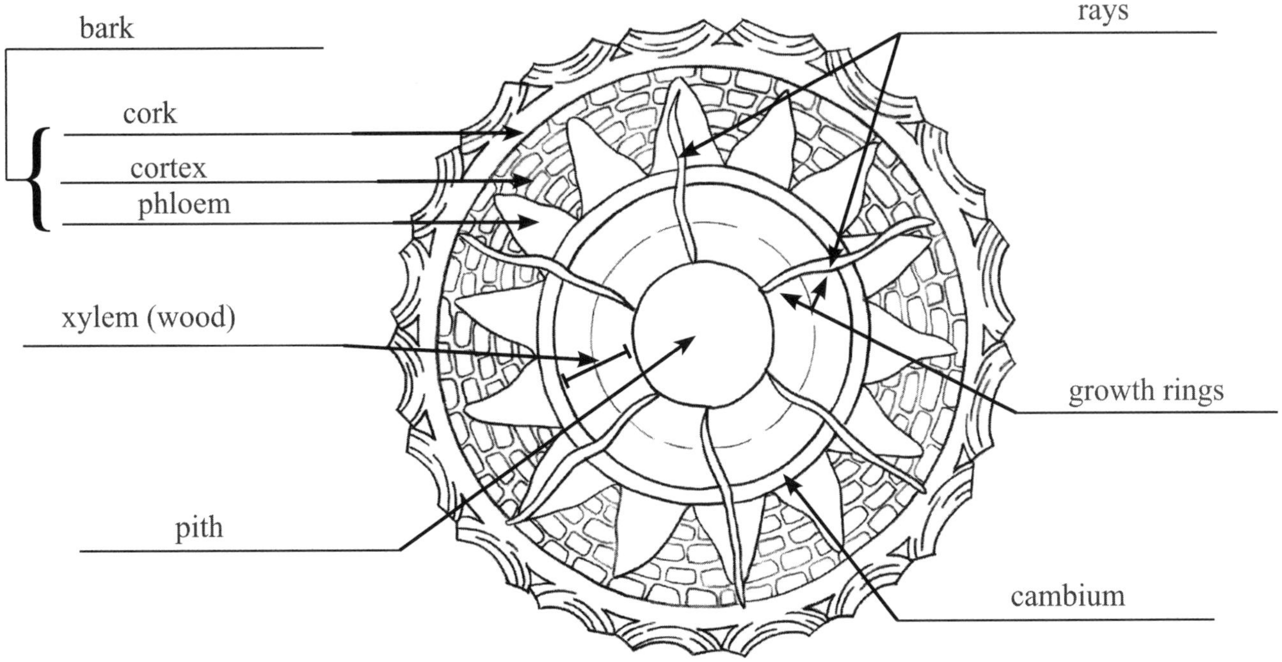

bark

rays

cork

cortex

phloem

xylem (wood)

growth rings

pith

cambium

III. Matching

_____J_____ **1.** transports food made in the leaves down to the stem and roots

_____H_____ **2.** a structure of tissue that performs a particular function in an organism

_____B_____ **3.** a plant life cycle that takes two years to complete

_____C_____ **4.** a ring of cells that separates the phloem from the xylem and creates new layers of xylem in woody plants

_____E_____ **5.** small units of life that make up larger organisms

_____L_____ **6.** anchors the plant to the ground and absorbs water and nutrients from the ground

_____A_____ **7.** a plant life cycle that takes a year to complete

_____P_____ **8.** transports water absorbed by the roots to the rest of the plant

_____O_____ **9.** a group of organs that work together to perform a particular function for an organism

_____N_____ **10.** supports the leaves and reproductive parts of the plant, transports food and water, and acts as a storage facility for food

_____M_____ **11.** sticky substance that flows through phloem

_____F_____ **12.** thickened layer of cells that provides protection for the root and herbaceous stems

_____G_____ **13.** substance contained in the xylem of all woody plants

_____K_____ **14.** spongy layer that stores water, but eventually disappears in a woody stem

_____D_____ **15.** a layer of thinly walled cells that store food

_____I_____ **16.** a plant life cycle that takes more than two years to complete

A. annual
B. biennial
C. cambium
D. cortex
E. cells
F. epidermis
G. lignin
H. organ
I. perennial
J. phloem
K. pith
L. roots
M. sap
N. stem
O. system
P. xylem

IV. Short Answer

1. What are the two systems found in plants? __root system and shoot system__

2. What are the organs that make up the shoot system? __stem, leaf, and flower__

3. What are the two types of plant stems? __herbaceous and woody__

4. What are the three areas of a woody stem? __bark, wood, and pith__

V. Extra Credit

1. What is the difference between heartwood and sapwood? __Heartwood is rings of wood that__ __no longer carry water. Sapwood is rings of wood that still carry water.__

2. What are the different bark textures? __smooth, fissured, scaly, or warty__

3. A tree begins its life with what type of root system? __a taproot__

Lesson 6 Quiz: *External Structure of Leaf I*

Name: **KEY**   Date: _____   Score: _____

I. Label the different leaf shapes.

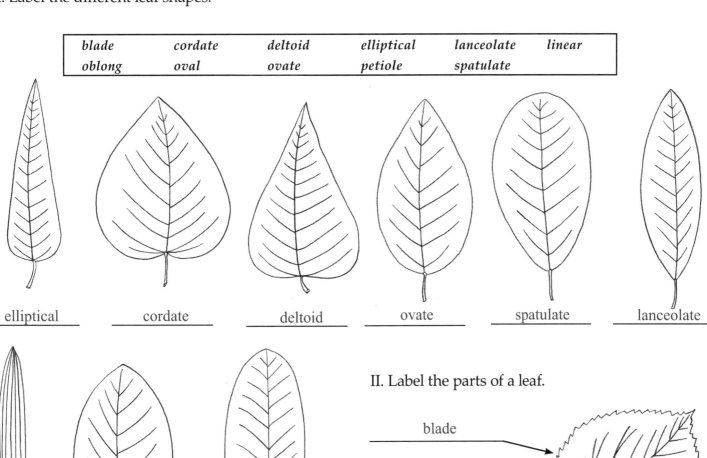

| blade | cordate | deltoid | elliptical | lanceolate | linear |
| oblong | oval | ovate | petiole | spatulate | |

elliptical   cordate   deltoid   ovate   spatulate   lanceolate

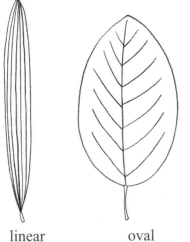

linear   oval   oblong

II. Label the parts of a leaf.

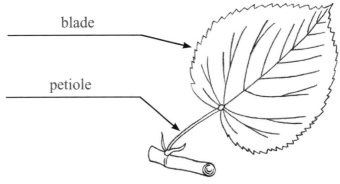

blade

petiole

III. Short Answer

1. What is the primary function of the leaf? The primary function of the leaf is to produce food for the rest of the plant by means of photosynthesis.

2. What are the two major categories of leaves? broadleaf and needle-leaf

3. Trees that lose their leaves in the winter: deciduous

4. Trees that keep their leaves during the winter: evergreen

5. Trees with needle-leaves: conifers

6. What are the different leaf textures? smooth, rough, fuzzy, hairy, or waxy

Lesson 7 Quiz: *External Structure of Leaf II*

Name: _____**KEY**_____   Date: _____   Score: _____

alternate	*bud scar*	*entire*	*internode*	*lateral bud*	*leaflet*
lobed	*opposite*	*palmate*	*parallel*	*pinnate*	*rachis*
subleaflet	*terminal bud*	*toothed*	*whorled*		

I. Label the types of leaf arrangement.

II. Label the parts of a branch.

opposite   whorled   alternate

terminal bud

lateral bud

leaf scar

internode

III. Label the venation and margin.

venation: __palmate__

margin: __lobed/toothed__

midrib

venation: __pinnate__

margin: __toothed__

IV. Label the parts of a compound leaf.

subleaflet

leaflet

rachis

venation: __parallel__

margin: __entire__

V. Short Answer

1. The place at which a leaf or leaves grow on a branch is called the _____**node**_____

2. The angle at which the leaf grows from the branch is called the _____**axil**_____.

3. Into what can a leaf bud grow? _____a leaf, a flower, or a branch_____

4. A leaf that is neither compound nor twice compound is called _____simple_____

Lesson 8 Quiz: *Internal Structure of Leaf*

Name: _____**KEY**_____   Date: _____   Score: _____

| cuticle | guard cells | lower epidermis | mesophyll | palisade layer |
| spongy layer | stoma | upper epidermis | vein | xylem & phloem |

I. Label the internal parts of a leaf.

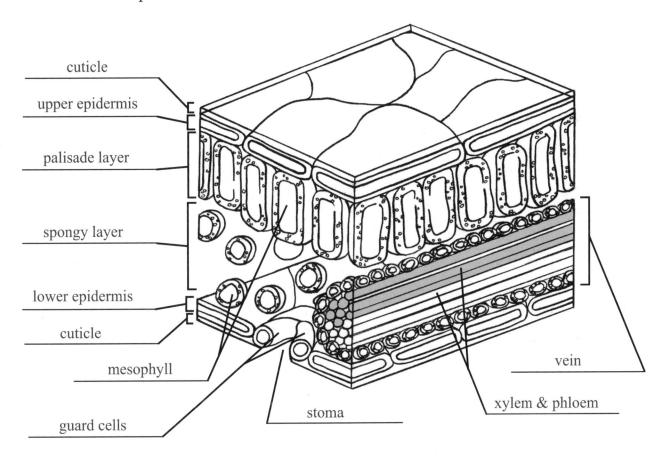

- cuticle
- upper epidermis
- palisade layer
- spongy layer
- lower epidermis
- cuticle
- mesophyll
- guard cells
- stoma
- vein
- xylem & phloem

II. Short Answer

1. What is the primary function of leaves? __to make food by means of photosynthesis__

2. What is the function of stomata? __The stomata open and close in order to take in the CO_2 and release oxygen.__

3. What three elements are required for photosynthesis? __sunlight, water, and CO_2__

4. _____Guard cells_____ open and close the stomata so that the leaf doesn't dry out.

5. The cells that give color to the leaf are called _____mesophyll_____.

6. Mesophyll cells have little food-making factories called _____chloroplasts_____ that contain the enzyme _____chlorophyll_____, which performs the process of photosynthesis and gives leaves their green color.

Unit II Test

Name: _____**KEY**_____   Date: _____   Score: _____

I. Match the leaf shapes.

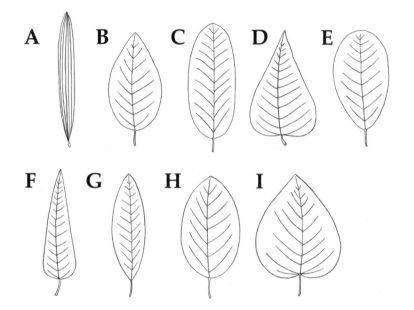

___I___	**1.** cordate
___D___	**2.** deltoid
___F___	**3.** elliptical
___G___	**4.** lanceolate
___A___	**5.** linear
___C___	**6.** oblong
___H___	**7.** oval
___B___	**8.** ovate
___E___	**9.** spatulate

II. Label the venation, margin, and parts of a leaf.

blade	*entire*	*lobed*	*midrib*	*parallel*
palmate	*petiole*	*pinnate*	*toothed*	

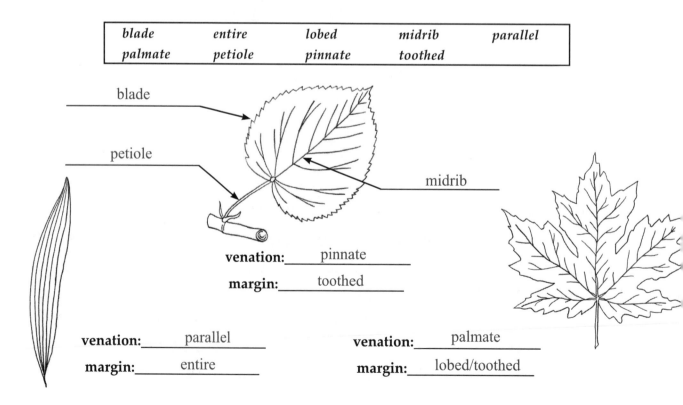

blade

petiole

midrib

venation:_____pinnate_____

margin:_____toothed_____

venation:_____parallel_____

margin:_____entire_____

venation:_____palmate_____

margin:_____lobed/toothed_____

alternate	*bud scar*	*cuticle*	*guard cells*	*internode*	*lateral bud*
leaflet	*lower epidermis*	*mesophyll*	*palisade layer*	*opposite*	*palmately compound*
parallel	*pinnately compound*	*rachis*	*spongy layer*	*stoma*	*twice compound*
terminal bud	*upper epidermis*	*vein*	*whorled*	*subleaflet*	*xylem & phloem*

III. Label the following diagrams for leaf arrangement, parts of a branch, parts of compound leaf, and
   internal parts of a leaf.

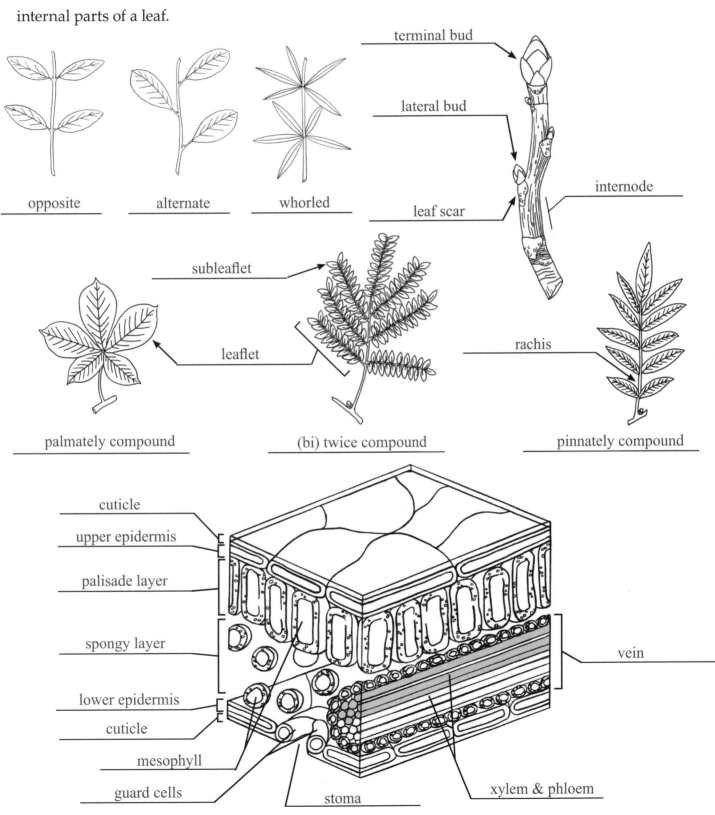

opposite   alternate   whorled

terminal bud

lateral bud

internode

leaf scar

subleaflet

leaflet

rachis

palmately compound   (bi) twice compound   pinnately compound

cuticle

upper epidermis

palisade layer

spongy layer

lower epidermis

cuticle

mesophyll

guard cells

stoma

vein

xylem & phloem

IV. Matching

_____O_____ **1.** arrangement of veins in a leaf

_____H_____ **2.** "like a palm"

_____M_____ **3.** tiny openings in the bottom of a leaf that allow gases in and out

_____E_____ **4.** a tree with needle-leaves

_____I_____ **5.** transports food made in the leaves down to the stem and roots

_____J_____ **6.** "like a feather"

_____F_____ **7.** trees that shed their leaves in the winter

_____B_____ **8.** enzyme in the mesophyll that gives the cell its green color

_____K_____ **9.** a leaf with no petiole

_____P_____ **10.** transports water absorbed by the roots to the rest of the plant

_____A_____ **11.** angle at which a leaf grows from the branch

_____D_____ **12.** a leaf with multiple blades for every petiole

_____C_____ **13.** factory-like parts of the mesophyll in which photosynthesis takes place

_____G_____ **14.** trees that keep their leaves during the winter

_____N_____ **15.** vascular structures that contain the xylem and phloem

_____L_____ **16.** a leaf with a single blade for every petiole

A. axil
B. chlorophyll
C. chloroplast
D. compound
E. conifer
F. deciduous
G. evergreen
H. palmate
I. phloem
J. pinnate
K. sessile
L. simple
M. stomata
N. veins
O. venation
P. xylem

V. Short Answer

1. What are the two major categories of leaves?____broadleaf and needle-leaf_____

2. What is the primary function of leaves? ___The primary function of leaves is to make food by the_ process of photosynthesis.

3. What three elements are needed for photosynthesis? ___sunlight, water, and CO_2_____

4. Into what can a leaf bud grow? ____a new leaf, branch, or flower_____

VI. Extra Credit

1. What is the difference between hardwood and softwood, and why is that distinction misleading? Hardwood comes from trees with broadleaves, and softwood comes from trees with needle-leaves. Some conifers have wood that is actually harder than some broadleaf trees. Thus the terms "hardwood" and "softwood" are confusing or poorly given names.

2. Why can't you see the other pigments present in the leaf? As long as photosynthesis is occurring, there will be far more chlorophyll than any other pigment. Thus, you can only see the other pigments when the chloroplasts stop performing photosynthesis.

Lesson 10 Quiz: *Structure of Flowers &*
Perfect Flower

Name: _____**KEY**_____ Date: _____ Score: _____

anther	female cone	filament	male cone	ovary	peduncle
perfect	petal	pistil	pistillate	receptacle	sepal
stamen	staminate	stigma	style		

I. Label the parts of a flower.

petal

stigma

anther

filament

style

stamen

ovary

sepal

pistil   receptacle

peduncle

II. Label the types of flowers.

III. Label the types of cones.

female

pistillate   staminate   perfect

male

IV. Short Answer

1. What is the function of flowers? ____Flowers produce seeds in order for the plant to reproduce.____

2. The process of producing organisms according to its kind: ____reproduction____

3. A flower's collection of petals is called its ____corolla____.

4. The male part of the flower produces ____pollen____. The female: ____egg cells____.

5. A scientist that studies plants: ____botanist____

6. A flower that has both male and female parts is called ____perfect____, and a flower that only has one or the other is called ____incomplete____.

7. Instead of flowers, ____conifers____ produce seeds by means of ____cones____.

Lesson 11 Quiz: *Pollination & Fertilization*

Name: _____**KEY**_____   Date: _____   Score: _____

anther	egg cell	filament	ovary	peduncle
petal	pollen	pollen tube	pollination	sepal
stamen	stigma	style		

I. Label the parts of a flower during fertilization.

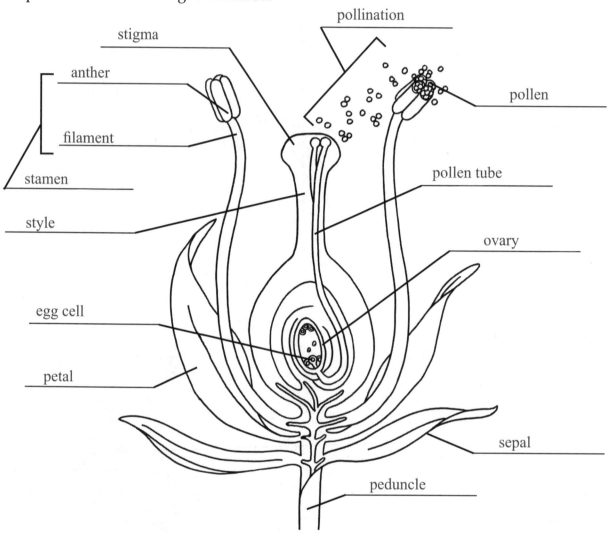

II. Short Answer

1. Male reproductive cells are called _____sperm cells_____.

2. The process in which pollen is transferred from an anther to a stigma: _____pollination_____

3. The sweet-tasting watery liquid produced by some flowers: _____nectar_____

4. Pollination that occurs by the help of insects and animals:_____biotic_____

5. Pollination that occurs by the help of wind and water: _____abiotic_____

6. The uniting of the sperm cells with the egg cells is called _____fertilization_____.

7. Fertilized egg cells will develop into _____seeds_____.

Lesson 12 Quiz: *Simple Fleshy Fruits*

Name: _____**KEY**_____   Date: _____   Score: _____

I. Label the following fruits according to whether they are berries, drupes, or pomes, and whether they are considered culinary fruits, culinary vegetables, or culinary nuts.

1. olive _____drupe; vegetable_____

2. watermelon _____berry; fruit_____

3. pear _____pome; fruit_____

4. grape _____berry; fruit_____

5. pumpkin _____berry; vegetable_____

6. walnut _____drupe; nut_____

7. plum_____drupe; fruit_____

8. jalapeño pepper _____berry; vegetable_____

9. banana _____berry; fruit_____

II. Short Answer

1. Fruit develops from the _____ovary_____ of the flower.
2. What is the function of a fruit? _____The fruit provides protection for the seeds as they grow and_____ then helps distribute the seeds once they are mature.
3. Seed-bearing structure that develops from the ovary of a flower: _____botanical fruit_____
4. Seed-bearing structure that is sweet in taste and fleshy in composition: _____culinary fruit_____
5. What are the three categories of fruit? _____simple fruits, aggregate fruits, and multiple fruits_____
6. A fruit that grows from a single flower with a single pistil: _____simple fruit_____
7. What are the two types of simple fruit? _____fleshy and dry_____
8. A simple fruit that is fleshy and juicy throughout: _____berry_____
9. A simple fruit that is fleshy with a stone in the center: _____drupe_____
10. A simple fruit that is fleshy with a papery inside layer:_____pome_____
11. An apple is formed from the entire _____receptacle_____ of the flower.

Lesson 13 Quiz: *Simple Dry Fruits; Aggregate & Multiple Fruits; & Dispersal*

Name: _____**KEY**_____ Date: _____ Score: _____

I. Label the following fruits according to whether they are legumes, samaras, nuts, achenes, grains, aggregate fruits, or multiple fruits.

1. raspberry _____ aggregate fruit _____

2. sunflower seed _____ achene _____

3. pea _____ legume _____

4. pineapple _____ multiple fruit _____

5. maple tree seed _____ samara _____

6. acorn _____ nut _____

7. wheat _____ grain _____

8. strawberry _____ aggregate fruit _____

9. rice _____ grain _____

10. peanut _____ legume _____

II. Short Answer

1. A simple dry fruit that consists of a pod enclosing several seeds: _____ legume _____

2. These pods can be _____ woody _____ or _____ herbaceous _____.

3. A seed with a papery wing that causes it to spin away from the tree: _____ samara _____

4. A simple dry fruit in which the seed is enclosed by a thick shell: _____ nut _____

5. A simple dry fruit with a thin shell that is mistaken for the nut: _____ achene _____

6. A simple dry fruit that comes from grass and has a thin shell that is attached to the seed:
   _____ grain _____

7. A cluster of individual fruit structures grown from the same flower: _____ aggregate fruit _____

8. A compound fruit that develops from a cluster of individual flowers: _____ multiple fruit _____

Unit III Test

Name: _____**KEY**_____   Date: _____   Score: _____

anther	egg cell	female cone	filament	male cone
ovary	peduncle	perfect	petal	pistil
pistillate	pollen	pollen tube	pollination	receptacle
sepal	stamen	staminate	stigma	style

I. Label the parts of a flower during fertilization, types of flowers, and types of cones.

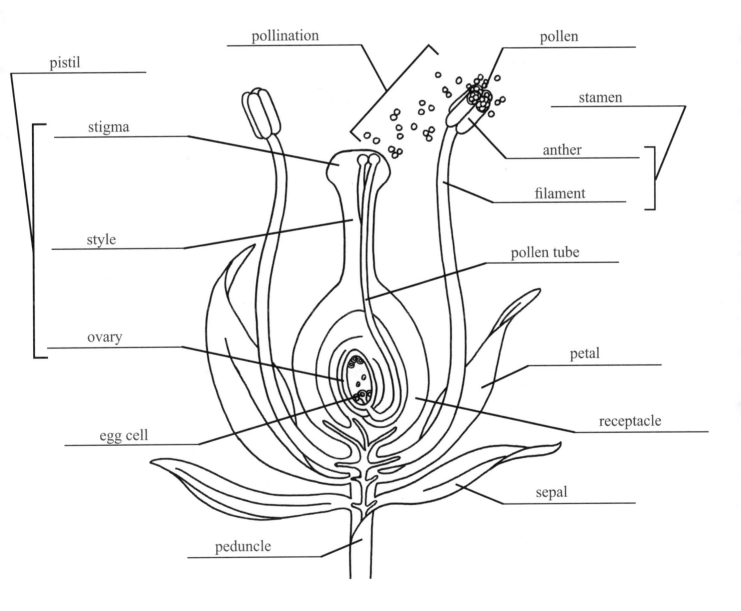

II. Label the following diagrams for types of flowers and types of cones.

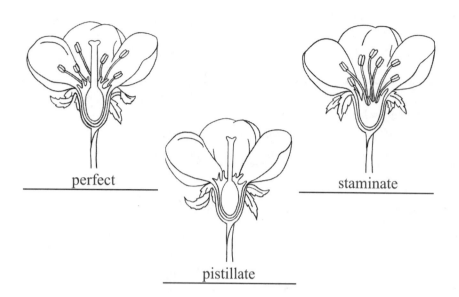

perfect

pistillate

staminate

female cones

male cones

III. Match the fruit to the correct description.

   H   **1.** simple, dry achene

   B   **2.** simple, fleshy pome

   J   **3.** simple, dry grain

   A   **4.** simple, dry nut

   I   **5.** simple, fleshy berry

   E   **6.** simple, dry legume

   F   **7.** fleshy, multiple fruit

   G   **8.** fleshy, aggregate fruit

   C   **9.** simple, fleshy drupe

   D   **10.** simple, dry samara

A.   acorn
B.   apple
C.   cherry
D.   maple tree seed
E.   pea
F.   pineapple
G.   strawberry
H.   sunflower seed
I.   watermelon
J.   wheat

IV. Short Answer

1. What is the function of flowers?   Flowers produce seeds in order for the plant to reproduce.

2. The ovary produces   egg cells , and the anther produces pollen .

3. What is pollination? the process in which pollen is transferred from an anther to a stigma

4. What is the botanical definition of a fruit? A fruit is a seed-bearing structure that results from the fully developed ovary of the flower of a plant.

5. What is the culinary definition of a fruit? A "kitchen fruit" is a seed-bearing structure that is sweet in taste and fleshy in composition.

V. Matching

_____D_____ **1.** simple fruit that is fleshy and juicy throughout

_____J_____ **2.** the uniting of a sperm cell with an egg cell

_____A_____ **3.** pollination that occurs without the help of a living thing

_____W_____ **4.** leaf-like appendages that protect the flower bud

_____Q_____ **5.** stalk that attaches the flower to the stem

_____B_____ **6.** simple dry fruit with a thin shell that is mistaken for the nut

_____V_____ **7.** seed with a papery wing that causes it to spin away from the tree

_____N_____ **8.** compound fruit that develops from a cluster of individual flowers

_____U_____ **9.** producing organisms according to its kind

_____O_____ **10.** sweet-tasting, watery liquid produced by some flowers

_____C_____ **11.** cluster of individual fruit structures grown from the same flower

_____Y_____ **12.** flower that only has the male part

_____M_____ **13.** simple dry fruit that consists of a woody or herbaceous pod enclosing several seeds

_____G_____ **14.** a flower's collection of petals

_____S_____ **15.** flower that only has the female part

_____I_____ **16.** simple fruit that is fleshy with a woody stone in the center

_____P_____ **17.** simple dry fruit in which the seed is enclosed by a thick shell

_____L_____ **18.** a flower missing either stamen or a pistil

_____R_____ **19.** a flower with both stamen and a pistil

_____T_____ **20.** simple fruit that is fleshy with a papery inside layer

_____H_____ **21.** having to do with use in the kitchen

_____X_____ **22.** fruit that grows from a single flower with a single pistil

_____E_____ **23.** pollination that occurs by the help of a living thing

_____F_____ **24.** what conifers use to produce seeds instead of flowers

_____K_____ **25.** simple dry fruit that comes from grass and has a thin shell that is attached to the seed

A. abiotic
B. achene
C. aggregate fruit
D. berry
E. biotic
F. cones
G. corolla
H. culinary
I. drupe
J. fertilization
K. grain
L. incomplete
M. legume
N. multiple fruit
O. nectar
P. nut
Q. peduncle
R. perfect
S. pistillate
T. pome
U. reproduction
V. samara
W. sepals
X. simple fruit
Y. staminate

VI. Extra Credit

1. Why are flowers' petals so colorful? __The different-colored flower petals attract different insects__ __and animals to the flower's pollen.__

2. Why is the nectar located at the bottom of the flower? __In order for an insect or animal to get to__ __the nectar, it must rub up against the anther, getting pollen on its body. When the insect or animal__ __goes to feed at another flower, the pollen on its body will rub off on the stigma of the other flower,__ __thus pollinating it.__

3. An apple is formed from the entire ____receptacle____ of the flower.

Trees Final

Name: **KEY**   Date: _____   Score: _____

alternate	anther	cambium	peduncle	xylem	twice (bi) compound
cortex	pith	filament	growth rings	leaflet	opposite
ovary	style	palmately compound	petal	phloem	pinnately compound
pistil	rays	rachis	receptacle	sepal	stamen
stigma	bark	subleaflet	whorled	cork	

I. Label the following diagrams for parts of a woody stem, parts of a flower, leaf arrangements, parts of a compound leaf, and the elements involved in photosynthesis.

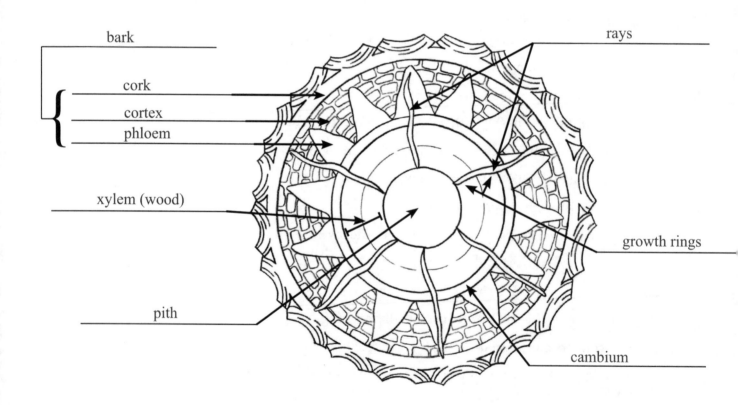

bark

cork

cortex

phloem

rays

xylem (wood)

growth rings

pith

cambium

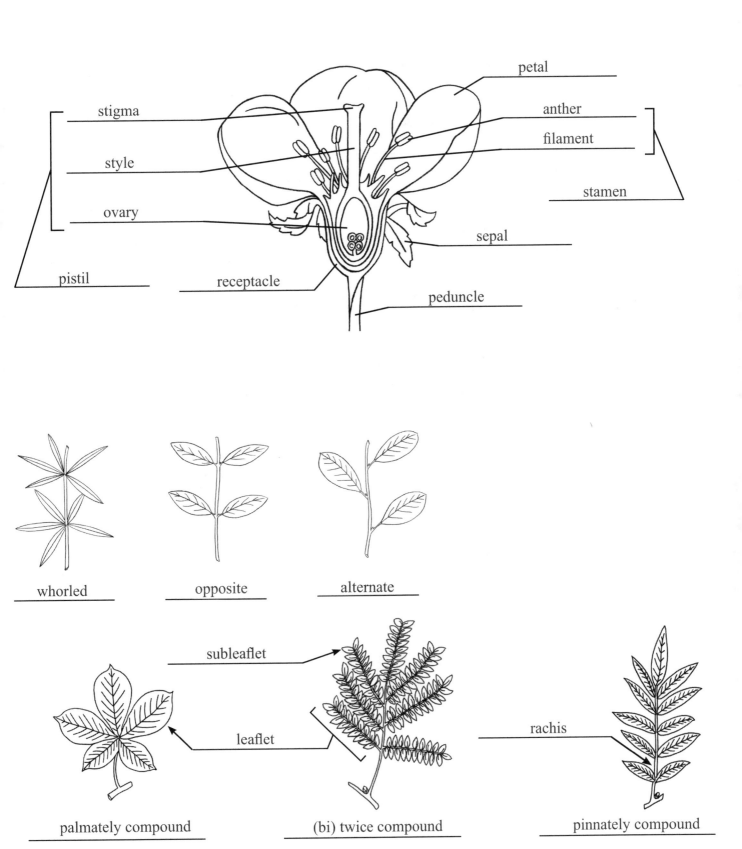

stigma

style

ovary

pistil

petal

anther

filament

stamen

sepal

receptacle

peduncle

whorled

opposite

alternate

subleaflet

leaflet

rachis

palmately compound

(bi) twice compound

pinnately compound

II. Short Answer

1. What are the two systems found in plants? _____root system and shoot system_____

2. What are the two types of plant stems? _____herbaceous and woody_____

3. What are the two major categories of leaves? _____broadleaf and needle-leaf_____

4. What is the primary function of leaves? _____The primary function of leaves is to make food by the process of photosynthesis._____

5. Into what can a leaf bud grow? _____a new leaf, branch, or flower_____

6. What is photosynthesis? _____It is the process by which leaves make food by means of sunlight and water._____

7. What is the function of flowers? _____Flowers produce seeds in order for the plant to reproduce._____

8. What is the botanical definition of a fruit? _____A fruit is a seed-bearing structure that results from the fully developed ovary of the flower of a plant._____

9. What is the culinary definition of a fruit? _____A "kitchen fruit" is a seed-bearing structure that is sweet in taste and fleshy in composition._____

III. Matching

G   1. a tree with needle-leaves

H   2. trees that shed their leaves in the winter

E   3. food-making factories in the mesophyll

I   4. trees that keep their leaves during the winter

P   5. transports food made in the leaves down to the stem and roots

B   6. a plant life cycle that takes two years to complete

C   7. small units of life that make up larger organisms

R   8. anchors the plant to the ground and absorbs water and nutrients from the ground

A   9. a plant life cycle that takes a year to complete

T   10. transports water absorbed by the roots to the rest of the plant

O   11. process in which pollen is transferred from an anther to a stigma

L   12. a plant life cycle that takes more than two years to complete

D   13. enzyme in the mesophyll that makes photosynthesis possible and gives green leaves their color

J   14. the uniting of a sperm cell with an egg cell

Q   15. producing organisms according to its kind

K   16. sweet-tasting, watery liquid produced by some flowers

S   17. flower that only has the male part

N   18. flower that only has the female part

M   19. a flower with both stamen and a pistil

F   20. what conifers use to produce seeds instead of flowers

A. annual
B. biennial
C. cells
D. chlorophyll
E. chloroplasts
F. cones
G. conifer
H. deciduous
I. evergreen
J. fertilization
K. nectar
L. perennial
M. perfect
N. pistillate
O. pollination
P. phloem
Q. reproduction
R. roots
S. staminate
T. xylem

IV. Extra Credit

1. What is the difference between a tree and a shrub? Trees have a single tall stem, whereas shrubs have several low stems branched near the ground.

2. How do you classify a tomato? The tomato is botanically a berry fruit, but is considered a vegetable when it comes to cooking. Thus it is a culinary vegetable.

Advanced Work

Quizzes, Test, & Keys

Lesson 17 Quiz: *Photosynthesis I*

Name: _____   Date: _____   Score: _____

carbon dioxide	chloroplast	energy	glucose	oxygen	water

I. Label the elements involved in photosynthesis.

II. Short Answer

1. The building blocks of life are called _____.

2. A group of atoms that all share the same characteristics is called an _____

3. What is a molecule? _____

4. In $C_8H_{10}N_4O_2$ (caffeine), how many atoms are present? _____
   How many elements? _____

Lesson 18 Quiz: *Photosynthesis II*

Name: _____   Date: _____   Score: _____

I. Write out the chemical equation for photosynthesis, and label both sides.

II. Based on the reactants, determine the number of molecules for each product.

$$2\ KClO_3\ \rightarrow\ \_\_\_KCl\ +\ \_\_\_O_2$$

Reactants: Products:
K = _____   K = _____
Cl = _____   Cl = _____
O = _____   O = _____

III. Based on the products, determine the number of molecules for each reactant.

$$\_\_\_Al\ +\ \_\_\_Cl_2\ \rightarrow\ 2\ AlCl_3$$

Reactants: Products:
Al = _____   Al = _____
Cl = _____   Cl = _____

IV. Short Answer

1. What simple sugar is produced by photosynthesis? _____

2. What is another name for table sugar? _____

3. Extra Credit: Balance this equation (both reactants and products).

$$\_\_\_\_N_2\ +\ \_\_\_H_2\ \rightarrow\ \_\_\_NH_3$$

Reactants: Products:
N = _____   N = _____
H = _____   H = _____

Lesson 19 Quiz: *Respiration I*

Name: _____   Date: _____   Score: _____

I. Write out the chemical equation for aerobic respiration, and label both sides.

II. Write out the chemical equation for fermentation and label both sides.

III. Short Answer

1. The process of releasing the energy in glucose for use in the cell: _____

2. Aerobic respiration requires _____ to break up the gulcose.

3. What is yeast? _____

4. What type of molecule is represented by the formula C_2H_5OH? _____

5. The three types of food energy are _____, _____, and _____, and they are all called_____.

6. What are the three types of simple sugars? _____

Lesson 20 Quiz: *Respiration II*

Name: _____   Date: _____   Score: _____

I. Short Answer

1. What are the three types of carbohydrates?_____

2. Another name for simple sugars:_____

3. Sucrose and maltose are examples of _____ (more than 1 sugar).

4. _____ is a _____ carbohydrate composed of many glucose molecules and is used in plants for storage.

5. _____ is a large carbohydrate that is found in plant cells.

6. Starch and cellulose are examples of _____ (many sugars).

7. _____ and _____ provide short-term energy, and _____ provide long-term energy.

8. What is an enzyme?_____

_____

9. Since cellulose can't be digested by humans, it functions as _____, which helps move other food through the digestive process.

10. Why are vegetables important to a healthy diet? _____

_____

Unit V Test

Name: _____ Date: _____ Score: _____

I. Label the elements involved in photosynthesis.

| carbon dioxide | chloroplast | energy | glucose | oxygen | water |

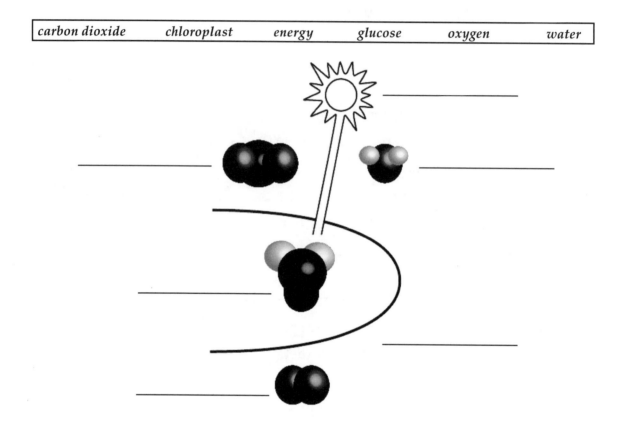

II. Write out the chemical equation for photosynthesis, and label the parts.

III. Write out the chemical equation for aerobic respiration, and label the parts.

IV. Write out the chemical equation for fermentation, and label the parts.

V. Matching

_____ 1. leaf cells in which photosynthesis takes place

_____ 2. a carbohydrate composed of many simple sugars

_____ 3. a combination of two or more atoms

_____ 4. carbon dioxide

_____ 5. chart that organizes the known elements

_____ 6. type of respiration that requires oxygen

_____ 7. glucose

_____ 8. building blocks of life

_____ 9. water

_____ 10. a single-celled organism that feeds on glucose

_____ 11. a carbohydrate composed of two simple sugars

_____ 12. enzyme in the mesophyll that splits and rearranges the molecules involved in photosynthesis

_____ 13. oxygen

_____ 14. any molecule with the atom ratio of CH_2O

_____ 15. another name for a simple sugar

_____ 16. alcohol

_____ 17. factory-like parts of the mesophyll in which photosynthesis takes place

_____ 18. type of respiration that uses yeast instead of oxygen and produces alcohol instead of water

_____ 19. a single molecule with the formula $C_6H_{12}O_6$

_____ 20. a group of atoms that shares the same characteristics

A. aerobic
B. atoms
C. carbohydrate
D. chlorophyll
E. chloroplast
F. C_2H_5OH
G. $C_6H_{12}O_6$
H. CO_2
I. disaccharide
J. element
K. fermentation
L. H_2O
M. mesophyll
N. molecule
O. monosaccharide
P. O_2
Q. Periodic Table
R. polysaccharide
S. simple sugar
T. yeast

VI. Short Answer

1. What is photosynthesis? _____

_____

2. What is cellular respiration? _____

_____

3. For what is glucose used in plants and animals? _____

_____

4. What are the three simple sugars? _____

5. What are the three types of carbohydrates? _____

VII. Balance these chemical equations.

$$2\ C_4H_{10} + 13\ O_2 \rightarrow \underline{\hspace{1cm}} CO_2 + \underline{\hspace{1cm}} H_2O$$

Reactants:

C = _____

H = _____

O = _____

Products:

C = _____

H = _____

O = _____

$$\underline{\hspace{1cm}} Si_2H_3 + \underline{\hspace{1cm}} O_2 \rightarrow 8\ SiO_2 + 6\ H_2O$$

Reactants:

Si = _____

H = _____

O = _____

Products:

Si = _____

H = _____

O = _____

VIII. Extra Credit

1. Why does bread rise?_____

_____

_____

2. Why do cooked vegetables taste slightly sweeter than uncooked vegetables? _____

_____

_____

_____

3. Balance this equation (both reactants and products):

$$\underline{\hspace{1cm}} Al + \underline{\hspace{1cm}} HCl \rightarrow \underline{\hspace{1cm}} AlCl_3 + \underline{\hspace{1cm}} H_2$$

Reactants:

Al= _____

H = _____

Cl = _____

Products:

Al = _____

H = _____

Cl = _____

Lesson 17 Quiz: *Photosynthesis I*

Name: _____**KEY**_____   Date: _____   Score: _____

carbon dioxide	chloroplast	energy	glucose	oxygen	water

I. Label the elements involved in photosynthesis.

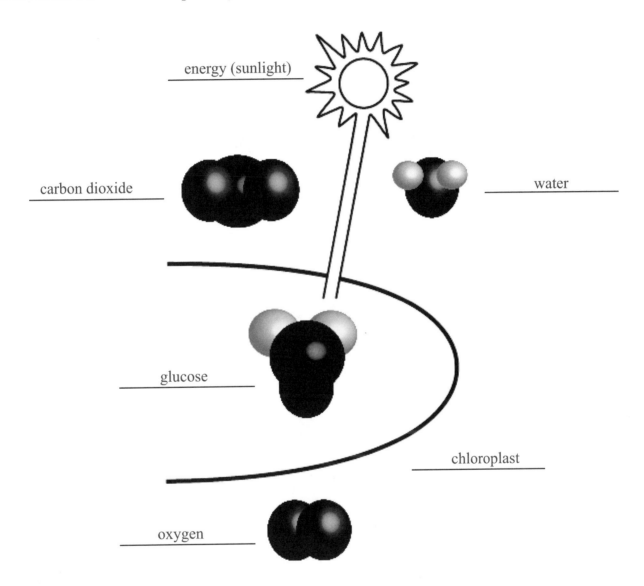

energy (sunlight) _____

carbon dioxide _____

water _____

glucose _____

chloroplast _____

oxygen _____

II. Short Answer

1. The building blocks of life are called _____atoms_____.

2. A group of atoms that all share the same characteristics is called an _____element_____ .

3. What is a molecule? _____It is a combination of two or more atoms._____

4. In $C_8H_{10}N_4O_2$ (caffeine), how many atoms are present? _____24_____

   How many elements? _____4_____

Lesson 18 Quiz: *Photosynthesis II*

Name: _____**KEY**_____ Date: _____ Score: _____

I. Write out the chemical equation for photosynthesis, and label both sides.

$$\overbrace{6\ CO_2 + 6\ H_2O}^{\text{reactants}} \rightarrow \overbrace{C_6H_{12}O_6 + 6\ O_2}^{\text{products}}$$

II. Based on the reactants, determine the number of molecules for each product.

$$2\ KClO_3 \rightarrow \underline{\ 2\ }KCl + \underline{\ 3\ }O_2$$

Reactants:
K = __2__
Cl = __2__
O = __6__

Products:
K = __1- 2__
Cl = __1- 2__
O = __2- 6__

III. Based on the products, determine the number of molecules for each reactant.

$$\underline{\ 2\ }Al + \underline{\ 3\ }Cl_2 \rightarrow 2\ AlCl_3$$

Reactants:
Al = __1- 2__
Cl = __2- 6__

Products:
Al = __2__
Cl = __6__

IV. Short Answer

1. What simple sugar is produced by photosynthesis? _____glucose_____

2. What is another name for table sugar? _____sucrose_____

3. Extra Credit: Balance this equation (both reactants and products).

$$\underline{\ 1\ }N_2 + \underline{\ 3\ }H_2 \rightarrow \underline{\ 2\ }NH_3$$

Reactants:
N = __2- 2- 2__
H = __2- 2- 6__

Products:
N = __1- 2- 2__
H = __3- 6- 6__

Lesson 19 Quiz: *Respiration I*

Name: _____**KEY**_____   Date: _____   Score: _____

I. Write out the chemical equation for aerobic respiration, and label both sides.

       reactants   products

$$C_6H_{12}O_6 + 6\ O_2 \rightarrow 6\ CO_2 + 6\ H_2O + energy$$

II. Write out the chemical equation for fermentation and label both sides.

       reactants   products

$$C_6H_{12}O_6 + yeast \rightarrow 2\ C_2H_5OH + 2\ CO_2 + energy$$

III. Short Answer

1. The process of releasing the energy in glucose for use in the cell: _____cellular respiration_____

2. Aerobic respiration requires _____oxygen_____ to break up the gulcose.

3. What is yeast? _____It is a single-celled organism that feeds on glucose._____

4. What type of molecule is represented by the formula C_2H_5OH? _____alcohol_____

5. The three types of food energy are _____sugars_____, _____starches_____, and _____cellulose_____, and they are all called_____carbohydrates_____.

6. What are the three types of simple sugars? _____glucose, fructose, and galactose_____

Lesson 20 Quiz: *Respiration II*

Name: _____**KEY**_____   Date: _____   Score: _____

I. Short Answer

1. What are the three types of food energy? _____simple sugars, starch, and cellulose_____

2. Another name for simple sugars:_____monosaccharides_____

3. Sucrose and maltose are examples of _____disaccharides_____ (more than 1 sugar).

4. _____Starch_____ is a _____complex_____ carbohydrate composed of many glucose molecules and is used in plants for storage.

5. _____Cellulose_____ is a large carbohydrate that is found in plant cells.

6. Starch and cellulose are examples of _____polysaccharides_____ (many sugars).

7. _____Monosaccharides_____ and _____disaccharides_____ provide short-term energy, and _____polysaccharides_____ provide long-term energy.

8. What is an enzyme?_____It is a special molecule that breaks starches apart into their individual simple sugars.

9. Since cellulose can't be digested by humans, it functions as _____fiber_____, which helps move other food through the digestive process.

10. Why are vegetables important to a healthy diet? _____They contain vitamins and minerals that are essential to human development and health.

Unit V Test

Name: _____**KEY**_____ Date: _____ Score: _____

I. Label the elements involved in photosynthesis.

| carbon dioxide | chloroplast | energy | glucose | oxygen | water |

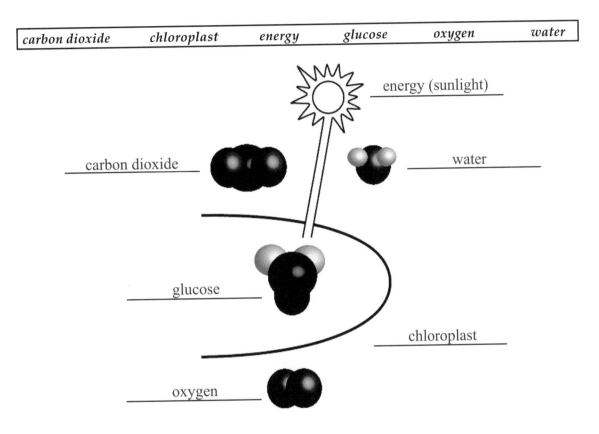

energy (sunlight) _____

carbon dioxide _____

water _____

glucose _____

chloroplast _____

oxygen _____

II. Write out the chemical equation for photosynthesis, and label the parts.

reactants   products

$6\ CO_2 + 6\ H_2O \rightarrow C_6H_{12}O_6 + 6\ O_2$

III. Write out the chemical equation for aerobic respiration, and label the parts.

reactants   products

$C_6H_{12}O_6 + 6\ O_2 \rightarrow 6\ CO_2 + 6\ H_2O + energy$

IV. Write out the chemical equation for fermentation, and label the parts.

reactants   products

$C_6H_{12}O_6 + yeast \rightarrow 2\ C_2H_5OH + 2\ CO_2 + energy$

V. Matching

_____M_____ **1.** leaf cells in which photosynthesis takes place

_____R_____ **2.** a carbohydrate composed of many simple sugars

_____N_____ **3.** a combination of two or more atoms

_____H_____ **4.** carbon dioxide

_____Q_____ **5.** chart that organizes the known elements

_____A_____ **6.** type of respiration that requires oxygen

_____G_____ **7.** glucose

_____B_____ **8.** building blocks of life

_____L_____ **9.** water

_____T_____ **10.** a single-celled organism that feeds on glucose

_____I_____ **11.** a carbohydrate composed of two simple sugars

_____D_____ **12.** enzyme in the mesophyll that splits and rearranges the molecules involved in photosynthesis

_____P_____ **13.** oxygen

_____C_____ **14.** any molecule with the atom ratio of CH_2O

_____O_____ **15.** another name for a simple sugar

_____F_____ **16.** alcohol

_____E_____ **17.** factory-like parts of the mesophyll in which photosynthesis takes place

_____K_____ **18.** type of respiration that uses yeast instead of oxygen and produces alcohol instead of water

_____S_____ **19.** a single molecule with the formula $C_6H_{12}O_6$

_____J_____ **20.** a group of atoms that shares the same characteristics

A. aerobic
B. atoms
C. carbohydrate
D. chlorophyll
E. chloroplasts
F. C_2H_5OH
G. $C_6H_{12}O_6$
H. CO_2
I. disaccharide
J. element
K. fermentation
L. H_2O
M. mesophyll
N. molecule
O. monosaccharide
P. O_2
Q. Periodic Table
R. polysaccharide
S. simple sugar
T. yeast

VI. Short Answer

1. What is photosynthesis? _____It is the process by which leaves make food by means of sunlight and water._____

2. What is cellular respiration? _____It is the process of releasing the energy in glucose for use in the cell._____

3. For what is glucose used in plants and animals? _____It is used for energy and the production of proteins, fats, vitamins, cellulose, and other materials._____

4. What are the three simple sugars? _____glucose, fructose, and galactose_____

5. What are the three types of carbohydrates? _____simple sugars, starch, and cellulose_____

VII. Balance these chemical equations.

$$2\ C_4H_{10} + 13\ O_2 \rightarrow \underline{\ 8\ }\ CO_2 + \underline{\ 10\ }\ H_2O$$

Reactants:
C = __8__
H = __20__
O = __26__

Products:
C = __1- **8**- 8__
H = __2- 2- **20**__
O = __3- **17**- 26__

$$\underline{\ 4\ }\ Si_2H_3 + \underline{\ 11\ }\ O_2 \rightarrow 8\ SiO_2 + 6\ H_2O$$

Reactants:
Si = __2- **8**- 8__
H = __3- **12**- 12__
O = __2- 2- **22**__

Products:
Si = __8__
H = __12__
O = __22__

VIII. Extra Credit

1. Why does bread rise? When yeast eats glucose, it produces alcohol and carbon dioxide. The carbon dioxide trapped in the dough causes it to fill with pockets of gas and rise.

2. Why do cooked vegetables taste slightly sweeter than uncooked vegetables? Applying heat to vegetables breaks up some disaccharides, like sucrose, or polysaccharides, like starch, into individual monosaccharides. Releasing the individual sugars in this way causes the vegetable or starch to sweeten in taste.

3. Balance this equation (both reactants and products):

$$\underline{\ 2\ }\ Al + \underline{\ 6\ }\ HCl \rightarrow \underline{\ 2\ }\ AlCl_3 + \underline{\ 3\ }\ H_2$$

Reactants:
Al= __1- 1- 1- 1- 1- **2**__
H = __1- 3- 3- **6**- 6- 6__
Cl = __1- 3- 3- **6**- 6- 6__

Products:
Al = __1- 1- 1- 1- **2**- 2__
H = __2- 2- 4- 4- **6**- 6__
Cl = __3- 3- 3- 3- **6**- 6__